Bizarre Cases

Contents

Mind Games

Introduction

B izarre Cases is the second collection of classic investigations of the paranormal culled from the pages of *Skeptical Inquirer* magazine, the official journal of the Committee for the Scientific Investigation of Claims of the Paranormal (CSICOP). CSICOP was founded by philosopher Paul Kurtz, together with scientists and scholars such as Carl Sagan, Sidney Hook, Stephen Jay Gould, and Isaac Asimov. The organization has worked to promote and defend reason and science in the battle against superstition, pseudoscience, and the paranormal.

In assembling this volume we have strived to give a sense of the breadth and depth of skeptical paranormal investigations. Many of these topics will be obvious candidates for inclusion, such as an analysis of the infamous Alien Autopsy film (page 40), ghost photos (page 66), or near-death experiences (page 148). Yet others are perhaps not so obvious, such as our sections on vampires (page 74), medical prayer (page 24), or urban legends (page 92). This array of cases was carefully chosen for not only the most bizarre phenomena and claims, but also the quality and thoroughness that set these skeptical writings apart from the mystery-mongering dross that spills from both supermarket checkout lines and best-seller lists.

We hope that these articles will foster a seed of skepticism in our readers, perhaps only a tiny voice inside that tells you that, when you hear fantastic and paranormal claims, you may not be getting the whole story. And that is what CSICOP and *Skeptical Inquirer* are all about: Giving readers the other side to the story.

ALTERNATIVE MEDICINE

What's That I Smell?

The Claims of Aromatherapy

by LYNN McCUTCHEON

Aromatherapy typically involves putting a few drops of some pleasant-smelling, plant-derived oil in your bath water, sniffing it from an inhaler, or massaging it directly into your skin. I sampled a number of these "essential oils," as they are called, and I was impressed with their unique aromas. So what's the problem with smelling something fragrant while you are bathing or while you are getting massaged? According to John Meisenheimer, who practices dermatology in Orlando, Florida, a tiny percentage of the population is allergic to some essential oils. But for the rest of us, the answer is, "nothing." A small dose of aromatic oil probably won't hurt you a bit, and if you enjoy the smell, that's fine!

The problem lies with the claims made by aromatherapy's most widely known practitioners—claims that are causally confused, ambiguous, dubious, and unsupported by scientific evidence. After reading several books and articles written by the enthusiastic supporters of aromatherapy, I believe that there are some recurrent themes that are worth a closer look.

One such theme is what I call "confused causation." Virtually all aromatherapists claim that if you relax for several minutes in warm bath water to which has been added a few drops of essential oil, you will get out of the tub feeling pleasant. I agree, but what causes the pleasantness? Is it the warmth, the water, the minutes spent resting, the few drops of oil, or some combination thereof? It would be easy to conduct an experiment in order to find out, but for some strange reason aromatherapists haven't seen fit to do this. Instead, they imply that the essential oil is the main cause. Says Meisenheimer: "The amount of essential oil from a few drops placed in your bath that might actually penetrate the stratum corneum [skin] is probably too small to have any meaningful, systemic, physiologic effect."

Other examples of confused causation permeate aromatherapists' writings. Hoffmann (1987, p. 94) claims that chamomile is good for insomnia if taken in a late bath. Is it the lateness or the chamomile that makes you sleepy? For stress, Lavabre (1990, p. 108) recommends relaxation, a better diet, nutritional supplements, more exercise, and a few drops of an oil blend. Heinerman informs us (1988, p. 197) that jasmine oil massaged into the abdomen and groin promotes sexual stimulation. I'll bet it does, with or without the jasmine. On page 301 he suggests that to make unsafe water safe, boil it and add rosemary, sage, or thyme before drinking. The heat probably kills most of the germs. Edwards (1994, p. 135) mentions that many patients in hospitals in England receive massages with essential oils. According to her, "the relaxing and uplifting effect of the oils helps boost the morale of the patients." Isn't it possible that the massage did as much to boost morale as the oils did?

One of the favorite tactics employed by aromatherapists is the use of ambiguous claims. Any good psychic can tell you that you never make a specific prediction. You always leave yourself enough room so that whatever the outcome, you can claim success. Judging from what I read, the aromatherapists have mastered this strategy. Here are some of my favorites, followed by my brief commentary.

According to Frawley (1992, p. 155), incense "cleanses the air of negative energies." What are negative energies? The reader is encouraged to get massaged with oil regularly (p. 155) because this "keeps the nerves in balance." How would we know an unbalanced nerve if we saw one? Hoffmann tells us (p. 95) that *ylang ylang* is "supposedly an aphrodisiac." Is it or or isn't it? Lavabre declares (p.114) that benzain resinoid will "drive out evil spirits." I'd love to see that. Presumably spruce oil is an even better essence because it is recommended (p.64) "for any type of psychic work." Why limit yourself to evil spirits? Edwards (p. 134) quotes Visant Lad as saying that "life energy enters the body through breath taken through the nose." Is life energy the same thing as oxygen, and if so, why can't it enter through the mouth? About tea tree oil, Edwards opines (p. 135), "There is hope [it] may play a role in the successful treatment of AIDS." Is it hope or is it evidence? On the same page she tells readers that aromatherapy is good for "restoring harmony and balance between the mind and body." Such a phrase can mean almost anything you wish.

Not all of the claims are hopelessly ambiguous or unlikely to be true. I did a computer search of the psychological literature back to 1967, using the terms *essential oil, aromatherapy,* and the names of 23 common essences. I found that chamomile (Roberts and Williams 1992) can put people in a better mood, and lavender sometimes causes mistakes in arithmetic (Ludvigson and Rottman 1989). Furthermore, several of the odors used by aromatherapists are capable of producing physiological arousal as measured by electroencephalogram (EEG) recordings (Klemm et al. 1992); and emotional

Patrick Hubenthal

changes, as measured by self-report (Kikuchi et al. 1992; Nakano et al. 1992). Peppermint odor appears to be capable of causing very small EEG, electromyogram (EMG), and heart rate changes during sleep (Badia et al. 1990); and some odors can modify artificially induced sleep time in mice (Tsuchiya et al. 1991). There is evidence that specific odors can better enable one to recall information that was learned in the presence of that odor (Smith et al. 1992).

As a whole, these findings stretched to the limit would support only small craft, sailing cautiously near the shores of the aromatic sea. Unfortunately, some aromatherapists have been more than willing to sail boldly into uncharted waters. Consider these claims about specific essential oils, with my comments.

"A few drops of jasmine (Tisserand 1988, p. 87) cures postnatal depression." I didn't find any olfactory research that mentions postnatal depression. "Marjoram oil (Tisserand, p. 37) turns off sexual desire." The few studies I found that mentioned marjoram had nothing to do with sex. Price (1991, p. 93) tells us that juniper berry is "relaxing" and "stimulating" (both?), and she (p. 48) and Valnet (1982, p. 87) recommend lavender for insomnia. The Klemm study showed that lavender was both arousing and unpleasant. Hoffmann (p. 94) claims that *patchouli* is good for anxiety. My computer search of the word *patchouli* turned up nothing. Valnet (p. 70) claims that *ylang ylang* is good for one's sex drive. *Ylang ylang* didn't turn up anything either.

Other claims of dubious validly are common to the writings of aromatherapists—broad claims that are related to the practice of aromatherapy in general. The following claims are my words, but they represent a synthesis of views expressed by the authors listed.

• *Smell is the most direct route to the brain.* (Avery 1992; Edwards 1994; Green 1992; Raphael 1994). The implication is that smell is superior to the other senses because olfactory information gets to the brain quickest, and since aromatherapy is concerned with smell, it is a superior method of treatment. Olfactory information gets to the brain very quickly, but so does auditory, tactile, and visual information. The differences would certainly be measured in milliseconds, and it would have no practical consequence. The olfactory sense is directly linked to the limbic system—a portion of the brain concerned with emotionally and memories. The aromatherapists make much of this—the smell of ginger evokes memories of grandma's cookies, etc. What they don't tell you is that the sight of grandma's photo or hearing her voice can do the same. All the senses are part of a massive network that links all parts of the brain. Smell enjoys no particular advantage when it comes to access to or speed of access to various parts of the brain.

• *Natural oils are better than synthetic ones.* (Avery 1992 Edwards 1994; Hillyer 1994; Lavabre 1990; Price 1991 Raphael 1994; Rose 1988). Most of these authors felt it unnecessary to explain such a statement, but Lavabre told readers that "natural" molecules work better because they have memory (p. 49). It is possible to make a synthetic preparation identical on a molecular level to the most important compound in an essential oil. John Renner, who has heard many of the bizarre claims made by aromatherapists, told me that if the molecules are the same, "I doubt seriously that your body could tell the difference." Given that essential oils contain several compounds, it seems possible that a natural oil might have more than one active agent. If that is so, then aromatherapists should be spearheading the research effort to determine which chemical compounds are inducing the changes they claim are taking place. Instead, most of them seem all too willing to assume that natural oils are better, and that there is no need to defend this assertion with any rationale or research evidence.

• *Essential oils can help your memory.* (Hoffmann 1987 Lavabre 1990; Price 1991; Valnet 1982). I found no evidence to support this, and none of these authors provided a hint about how they arrived at that conclusion. Psychologist Elizabeth Loftus, a world-renowned human memory expert, told me in a personal communication that she knows "of no cogent scientific evidence that smells cure amnesia, or that they strengthen memory." There is such a phenomenon as context-dependent learning. It has been shown that it is easier to remember X when you can return to the environment or context in which you learned X. Presumably, the context provides cues that make it easier to recall X. It has further been shown that at least one essential oil can serve as a contextual cue (Smith et al. 1992). If this is the basis for the above-mentioned claim, it is highly misleading. The essence itself is not important, only the fact that it was a significant part of the context in which the original learning took place. In other words, if the essence wasn't present when you learned X then it won't help you recall it later.

• *Scientists are doing a lot of research on essential oils.* (Avery 1992; Price 1991; Rose 1988; Valnet 1982). Statements like this are usually followed by specific claims. The implication is that these claims are supported by scientific research. As we saw earlier, that isn't necessarily true. Whether or not scientists really are doing a lot of research on essential oils is debatable. By comparison with fifty years ago, there is probably more research on essential oils today. By comparison with hearing and vision, research on the consequences of smelling essential oils lags way behind. If there really is a lot of research on the effects of essential oils, why is it that these authors are so reluctant to cite it? Their books and articles rarely list or mention any scientific journal articles. Instead, if there are any references at all they are to books written by other aromatherapists. All of this sounds as though I am strongly opposed to the use of essential oils. I'm not! If it pleases you to put some in your bath water or have a little rubbed on your back once in a while, by all means, go ahead. It is not the odor that arises from these fragrances that is troubling, it is the stench arising from the unwarranted claims made about them.

References

Avery, A. 1992. *Aromatherapy and You.* Kailua, HI: Blue Heron Hill Press.

Badia, P., et al. 1990. Responsiveness to olfactory stimuli presented in sleep. *Physiology and Behavior* 48: 87–90

Edwards, L. 1994. Aromatherapy and essential oils. *Healthy and Natural Journal,* October, pp. 134–137.

Frawley, D. 1992. Herbs and the mind. In *American Herbalism: Essays on Herbs and Herbalism.* ed. by M. Tierra. Freedom, Calif: Crossing Press.

Green, M. 1992. Simpler scents: The combined use of herbs and essential oils. In *American Herbalism: Essays on Herbs and Herbalism,* ed. by M. Tierra. Freedom, Calif.: Crossing Press.

Heinerman, J. 1988. *Heinermans Encyclopedia of Fruits, Vegetables, and Herbs.* West Nyack, N.Y.: Parker Publishing.

Hillyer, P. 1994. "Making $cents with Aromatherapy." *Whole Foods,* February, pp. 26–35.

Hoffmann, D. 1987. Aromatherapy. In *The Herbal Handbook.* Rochester, Vt.: Healing Arts Press.

Kikochi, A., et al 1992. Effects of odors on cardiac response patterns and subjective states in a reaction time task. *Pychologica Folia* 51: 74–82.

Klemm, W. R et al. 1992. Topographical EEG maps of human response to odors. *Chemical Senses* 17: 347–361.

Lavabre, M. 1990. *Aromatherapy Workbook.* Rochester, Vt.: Healing Atts Press. Ludvigson, H., and T. Rottman. 1989. Effects of ambient odors of lavender and cloves on cognition, memory, affect and mood. *Chemical Sense* 14: 525–361.

Nakano, Y., et al. 1992. A study of fragrance impressions, evaluation and categorization. *Pychologica Folia* 51: 83–90.

Price, S. 1991. *Aromatherapy for Common Ailments.* New York: Simon and Schuster.

Raphael, A. 1994. "Ahh! Aromatherapy." *Delicious,* December pp. 47–48.

Roberts, A., and J. Williams. 1992. The effect of olfactory stimulation on Fluency, vividness of imagery and associated mood: A preliminary study. *British Journal of Medical Psychology* 65: 197–199.

Rose, J. 1988. Healing scents from herbs: Aromatherapy. In *Herbal Handbook*. Escondido, Calif.: Bernard Jensen Enterprises.

Smith, D. G., et al. 1992. Verbal memory elicited by ambient odor. *Perceptual and Motor Skills* 74: 339–343

Tisserand, M. 1988. *Aromatherapy for Women*. Rochester, Vt.: Healing Arts Press.

Tsuchiya, T., et al. 1991. Effects of olfactory stimulation on the sleep time induced by pentobarbital administration in mice. *Brain Research Bulletin* 26: 397–401.

Valnet, J. 1982. *The Practice of Aromatherapy*. London: C.W. Daniel.

Magnetic Therapy:
Plausible Attraction?

by JAMES D. LIVINGSTON

A double-blind study at Baylor College of Medicine, published last November in *Archives of Physical and Rehabilitation Medicine* (Vallbona 1997), concluded that permanent magnets reduce pain in post-polio patients, and the results were heralded in *The New York Times* and on Bryant Gumbel's *Public Eye*. PBS's *Health Week* and *Time* magazine recently reported on the growing use of magnets by champion senior golfers and other professional athletes to relieve pain. Magnetic pain relief products are now sold in many golf shops, and ads for them appear in national golf and tennis magazines. Long a significant component of the health industry in Japan and China, magnetic therapy is becoming a more and more visible part of the alternative-medicine boom in the United States and Europe. Is it all just hokum, as many previously assumed, or is magnetic therapy becoming scientifically respectable?

Early History

For thousands of years, wonder and magic were associated with the mysterious forces exerted by natural magnets—magnetite-rich rocks, today called lodestones. Many trace magnetic therapy back to Paracelsus (1493–1543), a physician and alchemist who reasoned that since magnets have the power to attract iron, perhaps they can also attract diseases and leach them from the body. Charles Mackay, in *Extraordinary Popular Delusions and the Madness of Crowds* (1841), says of Paracelsus that "his claim to be the first of the magnetisers can scarcely be challenged." But Paracelsus was also aware of the important role of the patient's mind in the process of healing (Buranelli 1975). He wrote, "The spirit is the master, the imagination is the instrument, the body is the plastic material. The moral atmosphere surrounding the patient can have a strong influence on the course of the disease. It is not the curse or the blessing that works, but the idea. The imagination produces the effect." Paracelsus was apparently well aware of the placebo effect.

The development in eighteenth-century England of carbon-steel permanent magnets more powerful than lodestones brought renewed interest in the possible healing powers of magnets, and among those interested was Maximilian Hell, a professor of astronomy at the University of Vienna. Hell claimed several cures using steel magnets, but he was rapidly eclipsed by a friend who borrowed his magnets to treat a young woman suffering from a severe mental illness. The friend was Franz Anton Mesmer (1734–1815), and Mesmer's success with the "magnets from Hell" led directly to his widespread promotion of his theory of "animal magnetism." Although he first used actual magnets, he later found he could "magnetize" virtually anything—paper, wood, leather, water—and produce the same effect on patients. He concluded that the animal magnetism resided in himself, the various materials simply aiding the flow of the "universal fluid" between him and the patients.

Mesmer became so successful in Paris that in 1784 King Louis XVI established a Royal Commission to evaluate the claims of animal magnetism, a commission that included Antoine Lavoisier and Benjamin Franklin among its members. They conducted a series of experiments and concluded that all the observed effects could be attributed to the power of suggestion, and that "the practice of magnetization is the art of increasing the imagination by degrees." Thomas Jefferson, arriving in Paris soon after the Commission report, noted in his journal: "Animal magnetism is dead, ridiculed."

Ridiculed, perhaps, but not dead. Mesmer himself faded from public view, but "magnetizing" persisted in various forms. Many early magnetizers evolved into students of hypnosis and developed various forms of hypnotherapy. (The trance induced in many of Mesmer's patients is thought to be what is now called a hypnotic trance, and most dictionaries today list mesmerism as a synonym for hypnotism.) One American who became interested in magnetic healing was Daniel David Palmer, who opened Palmer's School of Magnetic Cure in Iowa in the 1890s. His ideas developed into the system of hands-on therapy known as chiropractic. Others focused on hand gestures without actual touch, an approach recently reborn as "therapeutic touch." Mary Baker Eddy was "cured" by a magnetizer, but she later became convinced that cures could best be achieved through prayer, and founded Christian Science.

Most of these byproducts of mesmerism, like Mesmer himself, ceased to use actual magnets. But the development of electrical technology in the late nineteenth century impressed the general public with the mysterious powers of electric and magnetic fields, and therapeutic magnets had a rebirth, with many "doctors" promoting magnets to relieve pain, enhance sleep, and cure a wide variety of diseases. The most notable of these was Dr. C. J. Thacher, whom *Collier's Magazine* dubbed "King of the magnetic quacks" (Macklis 1993). His 1886 mail-order catalogue offered a variety of magnetic garments, and a complete costume contained more than 700 magnets, which provided "full and complete protection of all the vital organs of the body."

In the twentieth century, materials scientists and engineers have developed stronger and stronger permanent magnets—alnico magnets in the 1930s, ferrite (ceramic) magnets in the 1950s, and rare-earth magnets in the 1970s and 1980s. The latest rare-earth magnets, neodymium-iron-boron, are more than a hundred times more powerful than the steel magnets available in the last century to Edison, Bell, and C.J. Thacher (Livingston 1996). Both ferrite magnets and the latest "neo" magnets have had a tremendous impact on modern technology, but they have also restimulated interest in the use of permanent magnets for magnetic therapy. Most magnetic therapy products today, like most refrigerator magnets, contain inexpensive ferrite magnets, but many suppliers offer neodymium "supermagnets" in their top-of-the-line products.

Magnetic Therapy Today

Both ferrite and rare-earth magnets, unlike earlier magnetic materials such as steels and alnicos, have great resistance to demagnetization, allowing thin disks to be magnetized. (Earlier magnets had to be long and thin to avoid being demagnetized by the internal fields produced by the poles at the ends.) This feature allows modern magnets to be mounted in a variety of thin products that can be applied to the body with the magnetic field emanating from the surface.

Some suppliers recommend applying magnetic patches directly to your aches and pains, while others recommend applying small Band-Aid-like patches to acupuncture points. Magnetic belts containing sixteen or more magnets are purported to ease back pain, and similar magnetic wraps are offered for almost any part of the body, including hands, wrists, elbows, knees, ankles, and feet (magnetic insoles are particularly popular). For headaches you can wear magnetic headbands, magnetic earrings, or magnetic necklaces. (One company marketing magnetic necklaces provides simple instructions: the necklace should be put on as soon as the headache appears and removed as soon as it goes away. Since most headaches come and go, following these instructions precisely will clearly produce persuasive evidence of the necklace's efficacy.)

Many magnetic necklaces, bracelets, and earrings are formed from silver- and gold-rich magnetic alloys and promoted as both fashionable and therapeutic. One catalog claims magnetic earrings "stimulate nerve endings that are associated with head and neck pain," and magnetic bracelets "act upon the body's energy field" and "correct energy imbalances brought by electro-magnetic contamination or atmospheric changes." Larger items include magnetic seat cushions, magnetic pillows, and magnetic mattress pads, the last claiming to produce an "energizing sleep field." One supplier offers a PCD—Prostate Comfort Device for older men. If properly placed while you sit watching television or driving your car, you will no longer have to get out of bed several times a night to relieve yourself!

To avoid trouble with the Food and Drug Administration, most suppliers emphasize only "comfort" and usually specifically state "no medical claims are made." Some, however, are far less careful. One company in Kansas markets a book entitled *Curing Cancer With Supermagnets*. The authors of the book claim to have cured cancer simply by hanging a neodymium "supermagnet" around the patient's neck. The cancer discussed in the advertisement was a breast cancer, but they report that "the supermagnets influence the whole body" and "our method can cure all types of cancer."

Many magnetic therapy products have alternating arrays of north and south poles facing the patient. Some have detailed explanations of why a circular pattern of poles is optimal, while others offer poles in checkerboard or triangular patterns. Nikken, the Japan-based firm that has used a multilevel marketing scheme to expand from an annual business in the U.S. of $3 million in 1989 to $150 million today, primarily offers products with alternating poles.

One clear difference between such multipolar magnetic devices and unipolar devices (with only one pole facing the patient) is the "reach" of the magnetic field. The field from even unipolar magnets decreases very rapidly with increasing distance from the magnet, but the field from multipolar magnets decreases much more rapidly. If multipolar magnets really have any effects on the human body, they will be limited to depths of penetration of only a few millimeters. (Many refrigerator magnets are multipolar, which limits the thickness of paper they can hold to the refrigerator, but also limits the damage they can do to nearby credit and ATM cards.)

Other suppliers offer only unipolar magnets, and some emphasize the importance of having only south-seeking poles facing the body. Contrary to common scientific usage, they call south-seeking poles north poles. Since opposite poles attract, they argue that a pole that seeks south must be a north pole. (Here practitioners of magnetic therapy are perhaps more logical than mainstream science, which calls the south-seeking pole a south pole, requiring that the earth's magnetic pole in Antarctica is, by the standard scientific terminology, a north pole.) Dr. Buryl Payne, in his book *The Body Magnetic* (1988), argues that south-seeking poles calm tissue but north-seeking poles stimulate tissue, and you should therefore never expose tumors or infections to north-seeking poles. When I suggested to one practitioner that different effects from different poles seemed to violate basic rules of symmetry, he assured me that the rules were reversed in the southern hemisphere.

One of the most ardent advocates of magnetic therapy is Dr. William Philpott of Oklahoma, who publishes his own Magnetic Energy Quarterly. He is also on the board of the Bio-Electro-Magnetics Institute of Reno, Nevada, a nonprofit "research and educational organization" and an advisor to the NIH Office of Alternative Medicine. His wife happens to have a business selling "Polar Power Magnets." Dr. Ronald Lawrence of California is President of the

North American Academy of Magnetic Therapy and reports that he has successfully used magnets to relieve pain in hundreds of his patients. He is associated with Magnetherapy, a Florida company that markets "Tectonic Magnets." Both Dr. Philpott and Dr. Lawrence favor unipolar magnets.

The efficacy of magnetic therapy (or of any other medical treatment, mainstream or alternative) does not depend on our understanding the biological mechanism. Nevertheless most promoters of magnetic therapy recognize the need for offering some plausible explanation. The mechanism most commonly offered for various therapeutic effects of magnets is improved blood circulation, despite a lack of clear evidence for such an effect. Other suggestions include alteration of nerve impulses, increased oxygen content and increased alkalinity of bodily fluids, magnetic forces on moving ions, and decreased deposits on the walls of blood vessels.

The broadest explanation was presented by Dr. Kyochi Nakagawa of Japan, who claims that many of our modern ills result from "Magnetic Field Deficiency Syndrome." Earth's magnetic field is known to have decreased about 6 percent since 1830, and indirect evidence suggests that it may have decreased as much as 30 percent over the last millennium. He argues that magnetic therapy simply provides some of the magnetic field that Earth has lost.

Magnetic therapy is also prominent in the treatment of thoroughbred racehorses. An injured racehorse represents potential loss of a substantial investment, providing considerable incentive to try "alternative medicine" to supplement mainstream veterinary treatment. Magnetic pads for a variety of leg problems, magnetic blankets, magnetic hoof pads, etc., all get ringing endorsements from many horse trainers—and even some veterinarians. One marketer of magnetic products for humans reports that he first became convinced of their effectiveness when he used them on his ailing llama! Enthusiasts argue that the placebo effect could not be effective on horses or other animals, but forget that it may influence the human who is interpreting the effect of magnetic therapy on the animal.

The Baylor Study

These examples and the centuries-old connection between magnets and quackery, have led many to consider modern magnetic therapy as total hokum, with the many testimonials for the success of magnetic treatments explainable by placebo effects. But the Baylor study, seemingly a careful double-blind study, has surprised many.

The study was conducted by Dr. Carlos Vallbona on fifty post-polio patients at Baylor's Institute for Rehabilitation Research in Houston. Bioflex, Inc., of Corpus Christi provided both the magnets (multipolar, circular pattern) and a set of visually identical sham magnets to serve as controls. To keep the study

"double-blind" neither the patients nor the staff were informed as to which devices were active magnets, and which were shams. Before and after the forty-five-minute period of magnet therapy, the patients were asked to grade their pain on a scale from 0 to 10. The twenty nine patients with active magnets reported, on average, a significant reduction of pain (from 9.6 to 4.4), while the twenty-one patients with shams reported a much smaller average reduction (from 9.5 to 8.4). This is a substantial difference, and if the double-blind study was successfully conducted, cannot be explained by a placebo effect.

For a hardened skeptic, some doubts remain. Both Dr. Vallbona and his colleague, Dr. Carlton Hazlewood, had reported the successful personal use of magnets to relieve their own knee pains prior to the study, raising doubts as to their objectivity. Conscious or unconscious biases of researchers can have very subtle and unrecognized effects on the results of their studies, and a serious difficulty of conducting any double-blind studies with magnets is the ease of distinguishing active magnets from sham magnets (although the patients were reportedly observed during the therapy period to assure that they were not surreptitiously testing their magnets). Another difficulty of any studies of pain relief is the highly subjective nature of the data.

Despite these various reasons for caution, the results of this study have altered the views of many physicians. Dr. William Jarvis, president of the National Council Against Health Fraud, had formerly dismissed magnet therapy as "essentially quackery." He now tentatively admits that it may have value for post-polio pain.

More studies will be needed before magnetic therapy will be accepted by a majority of the medical community, and some studies are already underway. Last year the NIH Office of Alternative Medicine gave a million-dollar grant to Dr. Ann Gill Taylor of the School of Nursing of the University of Virginia to study the use of magnets to relieve pain. Among other things, she will be testing the effectiveness of magnetic sleep pads in relieving pain in patients suffering from fibromyalgia, a common disease involving joint and muscle pain. While we wait for the results of these and other studies, does what we know about magnetic fields and the human body make it plausible that magnetic therapy for pain might have a physical basis beyond mind/body effects?

Magnetic Fields and the Body

The electrochemical processes of the human body are extremely complex and incompletely understood, and physical effects of magnetic fields cannot be ruled out. Many thousands of papers have in fact been published on biological effects of electromagnetic fields, much of it focused on the effects of radio-frequency and microwave fields or, in recent years, on fields at power-line frequencies (fifty or sixty cycles per second). Studies of biological effects of steady magnetic fields (reviewed by Frankel and Liburdy 1996) have concentrated mostly on high fields of the level encountered in MRI magnets, typically of the order of 10,000 gauss (1 tesla). Unfortunately, research has been very limited at field levels typical of magnetic therapy products, most of which are limited to a few hundred gauss, even at the magnet surface. (Earth's field is a bit less than half a gauss.)

Viewed simply as inert material, the human body, like its primary constituent, water, is *diamagnetic*, i.e., weakly repelled by magnetic fields. In response to an applied magnetic field, the electrons in water molecules make slight adjustments in their motions, producing a net magnetic field in the opposing direction about 100,000 times smaller than the applied field. With the removal of the applied field, the electrons return to their original orbits, and the water molecules once again become nonmagnetic. (We perhaps should note that some promoters of magnetic therapy also promote "magnetized water." You can't magnetize water. Although water responds weakly to an applied field, the response disappears as soon as the field is removed.) Although the diamagnetism of water and most living things is very weak, a high-field electromagnet producing 160,000 gauss (16 tesla) at the center of the coil has recently been used to levitate not only water drops but also flowers, grasshoppers, and small frogs (Berry and Geim 1997), the "flying frogs" drawing worldwide media coverage. Since fields of that magnitude are required to balance gravitational forces, the much lower fields of magnetic-therapy devices can only produce diamagnetic forces that are thousands of times smaller than gravity. (The repulsive force will be proportional to the product of the field and the field gradient.)

Some dubious literature suggests that magnetic fields attract blood, citing all the iron it contains. However, iron in the blood is very different from metallic iron, which is strongly magnetic because the individual atomic magnets are strongly coupled together by the phenomenon we call *ferromagnetism*. The remarkable properties of ferromagnetic materials are a result of the cooperative behavior of many, many magnetic atoms acting in unison. The iron in blood consists instead of isolated iron atoms within large hemoglobin molecules, located inside the red blood cells. Although each of the iron atoms is magnetic, it is not near other iron atoms, and remains magnetically independent.

The net effect of the weak *paramagnetism* of the isolated iron atoms in hemoglobin is only a slight decrease in the overall diamagnetism of blood. Blood, like water, is weakly repelled by magnetic fields, not attracted.

Although most components of the human body and other living things are weakly diamagnetic, many organisms have been shown to contain small amounts of strongly magnetic materials, usually magnetite (Fe_3O_4). The most extreme case is that of magnetotactic bacteria, originally found in mud collected from the marshes of Cape Cod. Each contains a long chain of magnetite particles that interact strongly enough with Earth's magnetic field to orient the bacteria along the field. Magnetite crystals have also been found in pigeons, honeybees, many mammals, and even in the human brain, but in proportionately much smaller amounts than in the bacteria. It seems very unlikely that there is enough magnetite within the human body to provide a possible mechanism to explain magnetic therapy. However, if magnetite particles were located at strategic places, they could locally amplify the effects of low magnetic fields and, for example, modify ion flow across cell membranes, of the type involved with electrical transmission in nerve cells.

More likely mechanisms are those based on magnetic forces on moving charged particles, possibly including ions or charged molecules in flowing blood, moving across cell membranes, moving across synapses between nerve cells, etc., or those based on more subtle effects on biochemical reactions (Frankel and Liburdy 1996). Although no physical mechanisms for magnetic therapy have been established, the possibilities are numerous and complex. Only further clinical tests, carefully controlled to account for placebo effects, can confirm or dispute the results of the Baylor study and prove or disprove the claims of magnetic therapy.

Some media reports have not sufficiently distinguished the Baylor form of magnetic therapy, based on modest static fields from permanent magnets, with a more accepted form of "magnetic therapy" based on high pulsed magnetic fields from electromagnets (Malmivuo and Plonsey 1995). Pulsed magnetic fields are very different from static magnetic fields, because, via Maxwell's equations, time-varying magnetic fields induce electric fields. Electric fields have pronounced biological effects, particularly on nerve and muscle cells, as we have known since the days of Galvani and his twitching frogs' legs. Many years ago the FDA approved the use of pulsed magnetic fields in "bone growth stimulators" for the treatment of fractures that were slow to heal, and research on "magnetic stimulation"—pulsed magnetic fields applied to the brain or other components of the nervous system—has grown rapidly in recent years. Transcranial magnetic stimulation, in which the patient receives hundreds of magnetic field pulses of 1 tesla or more, each only a millisecond in duration, has shown considerable promise as a means of treating depression. However, these forms of pulsed-field magnetic therapy are based on biological effects of induced electric fields, and are very different from the use of the static fields from permanent magnets.

Conclusions

Claims of therapeutic effects of permanent magnets should still be regarded with considerable skepticism. Most of the many testimonials to the effectiveness of magnetic therapy devices can be attributed to placebo effects and to other effects accompanying their use. For example, the magnetic back braces used by many senior golfers may help ease their back pains through providing mechanical support, through localized warming, and through constant reminder to the aging athletes that they are no longer young and should not overexert their muscles. All these effects are helpful with or without magnets. One British study of pulsed-field bone-growth stimulators, which were approved decades ago by the FDA, found that they were equally successful when the devices were not activated (Barker 1984), and concluded that their effectiveness resulted from the enforced inactivity associated with their use, rather than from the pulsed magnetic fields.

The more extreme claims of magnetic therapy, such as curing cancer by hanging supermagnets around your neck, are not only nonsense but also dangerous, since they may divert patients from seeking appropriate treatment from mainstream medicine. Magnetic jewelry and most other magnetic-therapy products probably are harmless beyond a waste of money. Several years ago, a double-blind study found that magnetic necklaces produced no relief of neck or shoulder pain (Hong 1982).

The results of the Baylor study, however, raise the possibility that at least in some cases, topical application of permanent magnets may indeed be useful in pain relief, a conclusion that should be regarded as tentative until supported by further studies. Any mechanism for such an effect remains mysterious, but an effect of static magnetic fields on the complex electrochemical processes of the human body is not impossible. My own guess is that inexpensive refrigerator magnets are as likely to provide help as the more expensive magnets marketed specifically for therapy. (But since human nature leads us to expect more from more expensive items, use of refrigerator magnets will probably decrease the placebo effect!)

References

Barker, A. T. et al. 1984. Pulsed magnetic field therapy for tibial non-union. *Lancet* 994–996.

Berry, M. V. and A. K. Geim. 1997. Of flying frogs and levitrons. *Eur. J. Phys.* 18: 307–313.

Buranelli, V. 1975. *The Wizard from Vienna.* Coward, McCann & Geoghegan.

Frankel, Richard B. and Robert P. Liburdy. 1996. Biological effects of static magnetic fields (in *Handbook of Biological Effects of Electromagnetic Fields,* second edition, Charles Polk and Elliot Postow, eds. CRC Press).

Hong, C. Z. et al. 1982. Magnetic necklace: Its therapeutic effectiveness on neck and shoulder pain. *Archives of Physical Medicine and Rehabilitation* 63:162–164.

Livingston, James D. 1996. *Driving Force: The Natural Magic of Magnets.* Harvard University Press.

Mackay, Charles. [1841] 1932. *Extraordinary Popular Delusions and the Madness of Crowds.* Reprint, L. C. Page.

Macklis, Roger M. 1993. Magnetic healing, quackery, and the debate about the health effects of electromagnetic fields. *Annals of Internal Medicine* 118(5): 376–383.

Malmivuo, Jaakko and Robert Plonsey. 1995. *Bioelectromagnetism: Principles and applications of bioelectric and biomagnetic fields.* Oxford University Press.

Payne, Buryl. 1988. *The Body Magnetic* (self-published).

Vallbona, Carlos, Carlton F. Hazlewood, and Gabor Jurida. 1997. Response of pain to static magnetic fields in postpolio patients: A double-blind pilot study. *Archives of Physical and Rehabilitation Medicine* 78(11): 1200–1203.

Efficacy of Prayer

A Critical Examination of Claims

by IRWIN TESSMAN and JACK TESSMAN

The therapeutic power of prayer is a recurring theme among many proponents of alternative medicine. One can imagine a natural explanation for the alleged benefits: a psychological boost from the belief that a supernatural power is on your side. But what if you are unaware that people are praying for you? Such intercessory prayers could only work through a supernatural agency.

Investigating the efficacy of intercessory prayer was given scientific legitimacy by Francis Galton, the father of biometry and a central figure in the founding of modern statistical analysis. In classic memoirs, Galton (1872, 1883) argued that regardless of how the prayers "may be supposed to operate," the "efficacy of prayer . . . is a perfectly appropriate and legitimate subject of scientific inquiry" because it can be tested statistically, as he then demonstrated.[1]

A Landmark Study

A celebrated study performed at San Francisco General Hospital by Randolph C. Byrd reported that patients in a cardiac care unit received statistically significant benefits from intercessory prayers (Byrd 1988). That study has attained special status within the alternative medicine community and has been reprinted as a "landmark study" (Byrd 1997).

In the same skeptical spirit that motivates one to seek the flaw in the design of a perpetual motion machine, we have examined Byrd's study, as others have done (Posner 1990; Sloan et al. 1999; Witmer and Zimmerman 1991), to seek a natural explanation to rival the supernatural one.

We believe a serious flaw exists in his critical Table 3, a flaw that raises doubts about the table's validity. That table reports the overall outcome for patients admitted to the cardiac care unit. Upon admission, they were entered randomly into one of two groups: an intercessory prayer group or a control group (192 and 201 patients). The outcome was recorded as *good, intermediate,* or *bad.*[2] Byrd found that compared to the control group, the prayer group had an excess of good outcomes and a deficit of bad outcomes, a significant difference in favor of the prayer group with $P < 0.01$ (Byrd's Table 3). The study was necessarily intended to be double blind. Byrd writes: "The patients, the staff and doctors in the unit, and I remained 'blinded' throughout the study."

Unfortunately, that was not the case at a critical point. Byrd's Table 3, which might best have been constructed by a panel of "blinded" doctors, was constructed by Byrd alone. But it was done in response to criticism of an earlier version of his manuscript, the writing of which had already required that the code be broken. Thus Byrd was no longer blinded when he determined the answer to the key question of which did better, the intercessory prayer group or the control group (Byrd, personal communication).

Because the table was apparently constructed from computer-stored data using objectively stated criteria that did not involve Byrd in any personal evaluation of individual cases, the lack of blinding might have had no effect. Although blind evaluation is clearly preferable, the use of an unblinded analysis could be defended were it completely computer generated. However, the criteria he chose for evaluating the patients' outcomes were formulated after the data were collected and when Byrd was unblinded. That is an unreliable approach. The criteria should have been selected before the start of the study.

The claim of blindedness is erroneous in yet another respect (one aspect of which has already been mentioned [Witmer and Zimmerman 1991]). In his acknowledgments, Byrd thanks "Mrs. Janet Greene for her dedication to this study," but without any elaboration of her role. In a later publication (Byrd with Sherrill 1995) we learn that Janet Greene was hired ". . . to be our coordinator. . . . Janet entered names of all the volunteer patients into a computer that randomly divided them into two groups. . . . half of the patients—only Janet knew who they were—were prayed for daily by our intercessors. . . . She kept detailed records of all patients in both groups." Thus the very coordinator of the study was completely unblinded. Once patients were assigned to one of the two groups, Greene should have had no further contact with the hospital.[3]

Byrd's evidence for supernatural intervention, if true, would arguably be one of the most remarkable scientific demonstrations of the last millennium. To be credible, however, it requires, among other things (Posner 1990; Sloan et al. 1999; Witmer and Zimmerman 1991), considerably more attention to strict blindedness. In the absence of that credibility, its status, not to mention the "landmark" label, is highly dubious.

A Confirmation Attempt

Recently, another prayer study, broadly based on Byrd's (and the subject of numerous news reports in October and November 1999), examined 990 patients admitted to a coronary care unit (Harris et al. 1999).[4] The authors scored the effects of intercessory prayer on the occurrence of thirty-four adverse conditions (Harris's Table 3).[5] These are similar to the twenty-six conditions scored by Byrd (his Table 2).

Their general approach to scoring the efficacy of intercessory prayer is summarized as follows. "Since prayer was offered for a *speedy recovery* with *no complications* [our italics], it was anticipated that the effect of prayer was unlikely to be evident in any specific clinical outcome category (e.g., the need for antibiotics, the development of pneumonia, or the extension of infarction), but would only be seen in some type of global score."

Let us therefore look first at the speed of recovery. The length of stay in the coronary care unit decreased 9 percent in the prayer group, but with $P = 0.28$;[6] the length of hospital stay increased by 9 percent in the prayer group, but with $P = 0.41$ (their Table 4). Thus, by either measure the large P values indicate that the results are quite consistent with a null effect; thus there is no evidence that intercessory prayer confers any benefit (or harm) in speed of recovery.

Next we examine the results for two types of global scores. One is the Mid America Heart Institute–Cardiac Care Unit (MAHI-CCU) weighted score (their Table 4)[7] for the thirty-four adverse conditions. They call this score the "primary predefined end point" of their study. It shows an 11 percent advantage to the intercessory prayer group with $P = 0.04$.

Another type of global score arises from an evaluation of overall outcomes judged by a blinded panel to be either good, intermediate, or bad, each based on Byrd's criteria.[2] Whereas Byrd found a significant difference ($P < 0.01$) in *good* and *bad* outcomes in favor of the prayer group, Harris et al., using the same criteria, find no significant difference ($P = 0.29$, Harris's Table 5). Thus, not only do these results of Harris et al. fail to confirm the significant differences found by Byrd, they constitute a second set of results (the first being on speed of recovery) that shows no significant effects of intercessory prayer.

Thus Harris et al. make three major tests of the efficacy of intercessory prayer: speed of recovery scores (Table 4), MAHI-CCU global scores (Table 4), and outcome scores (Table 5). On the basis of just the MAHI-CCU scores taken alone with its barely significant $P = 0.04$ value, Harris et al. conclude there is a beneficial effect of intercessory prayer.

This argument is simply fallacious: where there are multiple tests it is incorrect to single out just one, ignoring others with large P values that indicate no significant differences between the groups tested. For example, if the three tests were completely independent, the probability that at least one of the three would show $P = 0.04$ purely by chance would be $1 - 0.96^3 \approx 0.12$, which is well above the conventional maximum value of 0.05 for significance. Though the tests are not independent, it is clear that the overall probability of observing that just one of these three tests favors intercessory prayer with P as low as 0.04 is well explained by pure chance.[8]

Conclusions

The tests of Harris et al., taken in their entirety, fail to show any significant benefit of intercessory prayer, *and* one of the tests directly contradicts Byrd's primary evidence for efficacy (his Table 3) that is the cornerstone of his "landmark study."

Acknowledgment

We thank Louis J. Cote (Purdue University) for extensive discussion and criticism.

Notes

1. Galton's retrospective analysis revealed no beneficial effect.

2. Here is how *good* and *bad* scores were achieved. The outcome was scored as *good* if only one of the following occurred: "left heart catheterization; mild unstable angina pectoris of less than six hours' duration; self-limiting ventricular tachycardia within the first seventy-two hours of myocardial infarction; supraventricular tachyarrhythmia; uncomplicated third-degree heart block requiring temporary pacemaker; mild congestive heart failure without pulmonary edema; no complications at all." The outcome was scored as *bad* if there occurred "nonelective cardiac surgery, readmission to the coronary care unit after a myocardial infarction with unstable angina, extension of initial infarction, cerebrovascular accident, cardiopulmonary arrest, need for artificial ventilator, severe congestive heart failure with pulmonary edema and pneumonia, hemodynamic shock due to sepsis or left ventricular failure, death."

3. Byrd might have gone further and designed his study so that no human would know, until the appointed time for breaking the code, which patients were in the test group and which in the control group. If the intercessors needed names for their assigned patients, pseudonyms could have been used without any human knowing to whom the pseudonyms referred. This should present no difficulty to the omniscient Judeo-Christian God to whom the intercessors were praying.

4. To help assure blindedness, not even the patients knew they were being studied. The requirement of informed consent was waived, in part, because it was felt that the study posed no known risk to either patient group.

5. The conditions include, for example, the need for antianginal agents, antibiotics, arterial monitor, vasodilation, antiarrhythmics, catheterization, diuretics, a permanent pacemaker, an interventional coronary procedure, intubation/ventilation, major surgery, and twenty-two others.

6. We calculate $P = 0.36$. Reminder: P is the probability of this result occurring purely by chance. Conventionally, a value of P greater than 0.05 attributes no statistical significance to the result.

7. An example of their scoring system: if "a patient developed unstable angina (1 point), was treated with antianginal agents (1 point), was sent for heart catheterization (1 point), underwent unsuccessful revascularization by percutaneous transluminal coronary angioplasty (3 points), and went on to coronary artery bypass graft surgery (4 points), his weighted MAHI-CCU score would be 10."

8. It is the responsibility of Harris et al. to calculate the overall P value.

References

Byrd, R.C. 1988. Positive therapeutic effects of intercessory prayer in a coronary care unit population. *Southern Medical Journal* 81: 826–829.

Byrd, R.C. 1997. Positive therapeutic effects of intercessory prayer in a coronary care unit population. *Alternative Therapies in Health and Medicine* 3(6): 87–91, November.

Byrd, R.C. with J. Sherrill. 1995. The therapeutic effects of intercessory prayer. *Journal of Christian Nursing* 12(1): 21–23.

Galton, F. 1872. Statistical inquiries into the efficacy of prayer. *Fortnightly Review* 12 (New series): 125–135.

———. 1883. *Inquiries into Human Faculty and Its Development.* New York: Macmillan and Co. 277–294.

Harris, W.S., M. Gowda, J.W. Kolb, C.P. Strychacz, J.L. Vacek, P.G. Jones, A. Forker, J.H. O'Keefe, and B.D. McCallister. 1999. A randomized, controlled trial of the effects of remote, intercessory prayer on outcomes in patients admitted to the coronary care unit. *Archives of Internal Medicine* 159: 2273–2278.

Posner, G.P. 1990 (Spring). God in the CCU? *Free Inquiry* 10(2): 44–45.

Sloan, R.P., E. Bagiella, and T. Powell. 1999. Religion, spirituality, and medicine. *Lancet* 353: 664–667.

Witmer, J., and M. Zimmerman. 1991. Intercessory prayer as medical treatment? An inquiry. SKEPTICAL INQUIRER 15(2): 177–180.

ALIENS

Abduction by Aliens or Sleep Paralysis?

by SUSAN BLACKMORE

If you believe one set of claims, nearly four million Americans have been abducted by aliens. This figure has been widely publicized and is often assumed to mean that millions of people have been visited by members of an alien species and, in some cases, physically taken from their beds, cars, or homes to an alien craft or planet.

Personal accounts of abduction by aliens have increased since the publication of Budd Hopkins's books *Missing Time* (1981) and *Intruders* (1987) and Whitley Strieber's *Communion* (1987). There is considerable variation among the accounts, but many fit a common pattern. Wright (1994) summarized 317 transcripts of hypnosis sessions and interviews from 95 separate cases and concluded, "Numerous entity types have been visiting our planet with some regularity" (Part 2, p. 6). However, the "gray" is clearly the most common alien and over the years a typical account has emerged (see, e.g., Mack 1994; Schnabel 1994; Thompson 1993).

The experience begins most often when the person is at home in bed (Wright 1994) and most often at night (Spanos, Cross, Dickson, and DuBreuil 1993), though sometimes abductions occur from a car or outdoors. There is an intense blue or white light, a buzzing or humming sound, anxiety or fear, and the sense of an unexplained presence. A craft with flashing lights is seen and the person is transported or "floated" into it. Once inside the craft, the person may be subjected to various medical procedures, often involving the removal of eggs or sperm and the implantation of a small object in the nose or elsewhere. Communication with the aliens is usually by telepathy. The abductee feels helpless and is often restrained, or partially or completely paralyzed.

The "gray" is about four feet high, with a slender body and neck, a large head, and huge, black, slanted, almond-shaped eyes. Grays usually have no hair and often only three fingers on each hand. Rarer aliens include green or blue types, the taller fair-haired Nordics, and human types who are sometimes seen working with the grays.

The aliens' purpose in abducting Earthlings varies from benign warnings of impending ecological catastrophe to a vast alien breeding program, necessitating the removal of eggs and sperm from humans in order to produce half-alien, half-human creatures. Some abductees claim to have seen fetuses in special jars, and some claim they were made to play with or care for the half-human children.

Occasionally, people claim to be snatched from public places, with witnesses, or even in groups. This provides the potential for independent corroboration, but physical evidence is extremely rare. A few examples of stained clothing have been brought back; and some of the implants have reportedly been removed from abductees' bodies, but they usually mysteriously disappear (Jacobs 1993).

Theories

How can we explain these experiences? Some abductees recall their experiences spontaneously, but some only "remember" in therapy, support groups, or under hypnosis. We know that memories can be changed and even completely created with hypnosis (Laurence, et al. 1986), peer pressure, and repeated questioning (Loftus 1993). Are "memories" of abduction created this way? Most of Wright's ninety-five abductees were hypnotized and/or interviewed many times. Hopkins is well known for his hypnotic techniques for eliciting abduction reports, and Mack also uses hypnosis. However, there are many reports of conscious recall of abduction without hypnosis or multiple interviews, and the significance of the role of false memory is still not clear.

Another theory is that abductees are mentally ill. This receives little or no support from the literature. Bloecher, Clamar, and Hopkins (1985) found above-average intelligence and no signs of serious pathology among nine abductees, and Parnell (1988) found no evidence of psychopathology among 225 individuals who reported having seen a UFO (although not having been abducted). Most recently, Spanos et al. (1993) compared forty-nine UFO reporters with two control groups and found they were no less intelligent, no more fantasy prone, and no more hypnotizable than the controls. Nor did they show more signs of psychopathology. They did, however, believe more strongly in alien visitations, suggesting that such beliefs allow people to shape ambiguous information, diffuse physical sensations, and vivid imaginings into realistic alien encounters.

Temporal lobe lability has also been implicated. People with relatively labile temporal lobes are more prone to fantasy, and more likely to report mystical and out-of-body experiences, visions, and psychic experiences (Persinger and Makarec 1987). However, Spanos et al. found no difference in a temporal lobe lability scale between their UFO reporters and control groups. Cox (1995) compared a group of twelve British abductees with both a matched control group and a student control group and, again, found no differences on the temporal lobe lability scale. Like Spanos's subjects, the abductees were more often believers in alien visitations than were the controls.

A final theory is that abductions are elaborations of sleep paralysis, in which a person is apparently able to hear and see and feels perfectly awake, but cannot move. The *International Classification of Sleep Disorders* (Thorpy 1990) reports that sleep paralysis is common among narcoleptics, in whom the paralysis usually occurs at sleep onset; is frequent in about 3 to 6 percent of the rest of the population; and occurs occasionally as "isolated sleep paralysis" in 40 to 50 percent. Other estimates for the incidence of isolated sleep paralysis include those from Japan (40 percent; Fukuda, et al. 1987), Nigeria (44 percent; Ohaeri 1992), Hong Kong (37 percent; Wing, Lee, and Chen 1994), Canada (21 percent; Spanos et al. 1995), Newfoundland (62 percent; Ness 1978), and England (46 percent; Rose and Blackmore 1996).

The Sleep-Paralysis Experience

In a typical sleep-paralysis episode, a person wakes up paralyzed, senses a presence in the room, feels fear or even terror, and may hear buzzing and humming noises or see strange lights. A visible or invisible entity may even sit on their chest, shaking, strangling, or prodding them. Attempts to fight the paralysis are usually unsuccessful. It is reputedly more effective to relax or try to move just the eyes or a single finger or toe. Descriptions of sleep paralysis are given in many of the references already cited and in Hufford's (1982) classic work on the "Old Hag." I and a colleague are building up a case collection and have reported our preliminary findings (Blackmore and Rose 1996).

Sleep paralysis is thought to underlie common myths such as witch or hag riding in England (Davis 1996–1997), the Old Hag of Newfoundland (Hufford 1982), Kanashibari in Japan (Fukuda 1993), Kokma in St. Lucia (Dahlitz and Parkes 1993), and the Popobawa in Zanzibar (Nickell 1995), among others. Perhaps alien abduction is our modern sleep paralysis myth.

Spanos et al. (1993) have pointed out the similarities between abductions and sleep paralysis. The majority of the abduction experiences they studied occurred at night, and almost 60 percent of the "intense" reports were sleep related. Of the intense experiences, nearly a quarter involved symptoms similar to sleep paralysis.

Cox (1995) divided his twelve abductees into six daytime and six nighttime abductions and, even with such small groups, found that the nighttime abductees reported significantly more frequent sleep paralysis than either of the control groups.

I suggest that the best explanation for many abduction experiences is that they are elaborations of the experience of sleep paralysis.

Imagine the following scenario: A woman wakes in the night with a strong sense that someone or something is in the room. She tries to move but finds she is completely paralyzed except for her eyes. She sees strange lights, hears a buzzing or humming sound, and feels a vibration in the bed. If she knows about sleep paralysis, she will recognize it instantly, but most people do not. So what is she going to think? I suggest that, if she has watched TV programs about abductions or read about them, she may begin to think of aliens. And in this borderline sleep state, the imagined alien will seem extremely real. This alone may be enough to create the conviction of having been abducted. Hypnosis could make the memories of this real experience (but not real abduction) completely convincing.

The Roper Poll

The claim that 3.7 million Americans have been abducted was based on a Roper Poll conducted between July and September 1991 and published in 1992. The authors were Budd Hopkins, a painter and sculptor; David Jacobs, a historian; and Ron Westrum, a sociologist (Hopkins, Jacobs, and Westrum 1992). In its introduction John Mack, professor of psychiatry at Harvard Medical School, claimed that hundreds of thousands of American men, women, and children may have experienced UFO abductions and that many of them suffered from distress when mental health professionals tried to fit their experiences into familiar psychiatric categories. Clinicians, he said, should learn "to recognize the most common symptoms and indications in the patient or client's history that they are dealing with an abduction case" (8). These indications included seeing lights, waking up paralyzed with a sense of presence, and experiences of flying and missing time. The report was published privately and mailed to nearly one hundred thousand psychiatrists, psychologists, and other mental health professionals encouraging them to "be open to the possibility that something exists or is happening to their clients which, in our traditional Western framework, cannot or should not be" (8).

The Roper Organization provides a service for other questions to be tacked on to their own regular polls. In this case, 5,947 adults (a representative sample) were given a card listing eleven experiences and were asked to say whether each had happened to them more than twice, once or twice, or never. The experiences (and percentage of respondents reporting having had the experience at least once) included: seeing a ghost (11 percent), seeing and dreaming about UFOs (7 percent and 5 percent), and leaving the body (14 percent). Most important were the five "indicator experiences": 1) "Waking up paralyzed with a sense of a strange person or presence or something else in the room" (18 percent); 2) "Feeling that you were actually flying through the air although you didn't know why or how" (10 percent); 3) "Experiencing a period of time of an hour or more, in which you were apparently lost, but you could not remember

Figure 1. Examples of a "gray" and several other imagined aliens, drawn by children aged 8 to 13.

why, or where you had been" (13 percent); 4) "Seeing unusual lights or balls of light in a room without knowing what was causing them, or where they came from" (8 percent); and 5) "Finding puzzling scars on your body and neither you nor anyone else remembering how you received them or where you got them" (8 percent).

The authors decided that "when a respondent answers 'yes' to at least four of these five indicator questions, there is a strong possibility that individual is a UFO abductee." The only justification given is that Hopkins and Jacobs worked with nearly five hundred abductees over a period of seventeen years. They noticed that many of their abductees reported these experiences and jumped to the conclusion that people who have four or more of the experiences are likely to be abductees.

From there, the stunning conclusion of the Roper Poll was reached. Out of the 5,947 people interviewed, 119 (or 2 percent) had four or five of the indicators. Since the population represented by the sample was 185 million, the total number was 3.7 million—hence the conclusion that nearly four million Americans have been abducted by aliens.

Why did they not simply ask a question like, "Have you ever been abducted by aliens?"? They argue that this would not reveal the true extent of abduction experiences since many people only remember them after therapy or hypnosis. If abductions really occur, this argument may be valid. However, the strategy used in the Roper Poll does not solve the problem.

With some exceptions,[1] many scientists have chosen to ignore the poll because it is so obviously flawed. However, because its major claim has received such wide publicity, I decided a little further investigation was worthwhile.

Real Abductions or Sleep Paralysis?

The real issue raised by the Roper Poll is whether the 119 people who reported the indicator experiences had actually been abducted by aliens.

Since the sampling technique appears to be sound and the sample large, we can have confidence in the estimate of 2 percent claiming the experiences. The question is, Have these people really been abducted? The alternative is that they simply have had a number of interesting psychological experiences, the most obviously relevant being sleep paralysis. In this case, the main claim of the Roper Poll must be rejected. How do we find out?

I reasoned that people who have been abducted (whether they consciously recall it or not) should have a better knowledge of the appearance and behavior of aliens than people who have not. This leads to two simple hypotheses.

The Roper Poll assumes that people who have had the indicator experiences have probably been abducted. If this assumption is correct, people who report the indicator experiences should have a better knowledge of what aliens are supposed to look like and what happens during an abduction than people who do not report indicator experiences. If the assumption is not correct, then their knowledge should be no greater than anyone else's—indeed, knowledge of aliens should relate more closely to reading and television-watching habits than to having the indicator experiences if abductions do not really occur.

I decided to test this using both adults and children here in Bristol. It might be argued that genuine abductees wouldn't be able to remember the relevant details so I needed to use a situation that would encourage recall. I decided to relax the subjects and tell them an abduction story, and then ask them to fill in missing details and draw the aliens they had seen in their imagination.

Method

Subjects were 126 school children aged 8 to 13 and 224 first-year undergraduates aged 18 and over. The children came from two schools in Bristol. They were tested in their classrooms in groups of 22 to 28. The first group of 22 children had a slightly different questionnaire from the other groups and, is therefore, excluded from some of the analyses. The adults were psychology and physiotherapy students at the University of the West of England tested in three large groups. The procedure for the children is described below. The procedure was slightly simplified and the story slightly modified for the adults.

I first spent about half an hour talking to the children about psychology and research so that they got used to me. I then asked them to relax—as much as they could in the classroom. Many laid their heads on the desks, some even lay down on the floor. I asked them to imagine they were in bed and being read a bedtime story. I suggested they try to visualize all the details of the story in their minds while I read it to them. I then read, slowly and clearly, a story called "Jackie and the Aliens," in which a girl is visited in bed at night by a strange alien who takes her into a spacecraft, examines her on a table, and brings her back unharmed to bed. The story includes such features as traveling down a corridor into a room, being laid on a table, seeing alien writing, and catching a glimpse of jars on shelves. However, precise details are not given.

At the end of the story, I asked the children to "wake up" slowly and to try to remember as much as they could of the details of the story. I then handed out the questionnaires. Each questionnaire contained five multiple-choice questions about the alien, the room, and table; and the children were asked to describe what was in the jars and to draw the alien writing. There were also six questions based on those in the Roper Poll: Have you ever seen a UFO? Have you ever seen a ghost? Have you ever felt as though you left your body and could fly around without it (an out-of-body experience, or OBE)? Have you ever seen unusual lights or balls of light in a room without knowing what was causing them, or where they came from? Have you ever woken up paralyzed, that is, with the feeling that you could not move? And, Have you ever woken up with the sense that there was a strange person or presence or something else in the room? (Note that in the Roper Poll, the question about paralysis was compounded with the question of the sense of presence. Here, two separate questions were asked. Note also that the last four of these questions were based on the *indicator* questions from the Roper Poll.) The questions were slightly altered to make them suitable for young children, and I did not ask about scars or missing time. A question about false awakenings (dreaming you have woken up) was also included, and two questions about television-watching habits.

Finally, all groups except one of the adult groups were asked to draw pictures of the alien they had imagined in the story.

Results

Large numbers of both adults and children reported having had most of the experiences. The percentages are shown in Table 1.

For each person, an "alien score" from 0 to 6 was given for the number of "correct" answers to the questions about the alien (that is, answers that conformed to the popular stereotype), and another score for the number of Roper Poll indicator experiences reported (0–4).

For the children, the mean alien score was 0.95, and the mean number of experiences 1.51. There was no correlation between the two measures

(r_s = −0.03, n = 101, p = 0.78). The drawings of aliens were roughly categorized by an independent judge into "grays" and "others" (for almost all drawings the category is obvious; see figure 1). Twelve (12 percent) of the children drew grays and 87 did not. Not surprisingly, those who drew a gray also achieved higher alien scores (t = 3.87, 97 df, p < 0.0001), but they did not report more of the experiences (t = 0.66, 95 df, p = 0.51).

Experience	Adults	Kids
Ghosts	14%	33%
OBEs	35%	33%
UFOs	8%	28%
False Awakenings	83%	57%
Sleep Paralysis	46%	34%
Presence	68%	56%
Lights	17%	28%

Table 1. Results of two surveys, with percentage of people answering "Yes" for having had the experience indicated. See text for full wording of questions.

Those children who drew grays did not report watching more television. Nor was there a correlation between the amount of television watched and the alien score (r_s = 0.002, n = 101, p = 0.98). Oddly, there was a small positive correlation between the amount of television watched and the number of experiences reported (r_s = 0.25, n = 101, p = 0.01).

For the adults, mean alien score was 1.23 and mean number of experiences 1.64. Again, there was no correlation between the two measures (r_s = 0.07, n = 213, p = 0.29). Seventeen of the adults drew grays, and 103 did not. Again those who drew a gray achieved higher alien scores (t = 6.11, 118 df, p < 0.0001) but did not report more experiences (t = 0.14, 115 df, p = 0.89).

Among the adults, those who drew grays *were* those who watched more television (U = 534, n = 100, 17, p < 0.01), and the amount of television watched correlated positively with the alien score (r_s = 0.20, n = 217, p = 0.003).

Discussion

These results provide no evidence that people who reported more of the indicator experiences had a better idea of what an alien should look like or what should happen during an abduction. If real gray aliens are abducting people from Earth, and the Roper Poll is correct in associating the indicator experiences with abduction, then we should expect such a relationship. Its absence in a relatively large sample casts doubt on these premises.

Among the adults (though not the children), there was a correlation between the amount of television they watched and their knowledge about aliens and abductions. This suggests that the popular stereotype is obtained more from television programs than from having been abducted by real aliens.

Our sample certainly included enough people who reported the indicator experiences. Although not all the indicator experiences were included, for the four questions that were used, the incidence was actually higher than that found by the Roper Poll. Presumably, therefore, many of my subjects would have been classified by Hopkins, Jacobs, and Westrum as having been abducted. The results suggest this conclusion would be quite unjustified.

These findings do not and cannot prove that no real abductions are occurring on this planet. What they do show is that knowledge of the appearance and behavior of abducting aliens depends more on how much television a person watches than on how many "indicator experiences" he or she has had. I conclude that the claim of the Roper Poll, that 3.7 million Americans have probably been abducted, is false.

Acknowledgment

I would like to thank the Perrott-Warrick Fund for financial assistance and Nick Rose for help with the analysis.

Note

1. For three earlier articles in the SKEPTICAL INQUIRER evaluating and strongly critiquing the interpretations of the Roper Poll, see Lloyd Stires, "3.7 Million Americans Kidnapped by Aliens?" 17 (2), Winter 1993; Philip J. Klass, "Additional Comments about the 'Unusual Personal Experiences Survey'," 17 (2), Winter 1993; and Robyn M. Dawes and Matthew Mulford, "Diagnoses of Alien Kidnappings That Result from Conjunction Effects in Memory," 18 (1), Fall 1993. All are reprinted in Kendrick Frazier, Barry Karr, and Joe Nickell, eds., *The UFO Invasion*, Prometheus Books, 1997.

References

Blackmore, S.J., and N.J. Rose. 1996. *Experiences on the Borderline between Reality and Imagination.* 20th International Conference of the Society for Psychical Research, Cirencester, 31 August 1996.

Bloecher, T., A. Clamar, and B. Hopkins. 1985. *Summary Report on the Psychological Testing of Nine Individuals Reporting UFO Abduction Experiences.* Mt Ranier, Md.: Fund for UFO Research.

Cox, M. 1995. *The Prevalence of Sleep Paralysis and Temporal Lobe Lability in Persons Who Report Alien Abduction.* Unpublished thesis, Department of Psychology, University of the West of England, Bristol.

Dahlitz, M., and J.D. Parkes. 1993. Sleep paralysis. *Lancet* 341(8842): 406–407.

Davis, O. 1996–1997. Hag-riding in nineteenth-century West Country England and modern Newfoundland: An examination of an experience-centred witchcraft tradition. *Folk Life* 35.

Fukuda, K., A. Miyasita, M. Inugami, and K. Ishihara. 1987. High prevalence of isolated sleep paralysis: Kanashibari phenomenon in Japan. *Sleep* 10(3): 279–286.

Fukuda, K. 1993. One explanatory basis for the discrepancy of reported prevalences of sleep paralysis among healthy respondents. *Perceptual and Motor Skills* 77(3, pt. 1): 803–807.

Hopkins, B. 1981. *Missing Time.* New York: Random House.

Hopkins, B. 1987. *Intruders: The Incredible Visitations at Copley Woods.* New York: Random House.

Hopkins, B., D.M. Jacobs, and R. Westrum. 1992. *Unusual Personal Experiences: An Analysis of Data from Three National Surveys Conducted by the Roper Organization.* Bigelow Holding Corporation, Nevada.

Hufford, D.J. 1982. *The Terror That Comes in the Night: An Experience Centered Study of*

Supernatural Assault Traditions. Philadelphia: University of Pennsylvania Press.

Jacobs, D.M. 1993.. *Secret Life: Firsthand Accounts of UFO Abductions*. London: Fourth Estate.

Laurence, J.-R., R. Nadon, H. Nogrady, and C. Perry. 1986. Duality, dissociation, and memory creation in highly hypnotizable subjects. *International Journal of Clinical and Experimental Hypnosis* 34: 296–309.

Loftus, E.F. 1993. The reality of repressed memories. *American Psychologist* 48: 518–537.

Mack, J.E. 1994. *Abduction: Human Encounters with Aliens*. London: Simon and Schuster.

Ness, R. 1978. The Old Hag phenomenon as sleep paralysis: A biocultural interpretation. *Culture, Medicine and Psychiatry* 2: 15–39.

Nickell, J. 1995. The skeptic-raping demon of Zanzibar. *Skeptical Briefs* 5(4): 7.

Ohaeri, J.U. 1992. Experience of isolated sleep paralysis in clinical practice in Nigeria. *Journal of the National Medical Association* 84(6): 521–523.

Parnell, J. 1988. Measured personality characteristics of persons who claim UFO experiences. *Psychotherapy in Private Practice* 6: 159–165.

Persinger, M.A., and K. Makarec. 1987. Temporal lobe epileptic signs and correlative behaviors displayed by normal populations *Journal of General Psychology* 114: 179–195.

Rose, N.J., and S.J. Blackmore. 1996. *Two Pilot Surveys of Unusual Personal Experiences*. 20th International Conference of the Society for Psychical Research, Cirencester, 31 August 1996.

Schnabel, J. 1994. *Dark White: Aliens, Abductions and the UFO Obsession*. London: Hamish Hamilton.

Spanos, N.P., P.A. Cross, K. Dickson, and S. C. DuBreuil. 1993. Close encounters: An examination of UFO experiences. *Journal of Abnormal Psychology* 102: 624–632.

Spanos, N. P., S. A. McNulty, S. C. DuBreuil, M. Pires, and M.F. Burgess. 1995. The frequency and correlates of sleep paralysis in a university sample. *Journal of Research in Personality* 29(3): 285–305.

Strieber, W. 1987. *Communion*. New York: Morrow.

Thompson, R.L. 1993. *Alien Identities*. San Diego: Govardhan Hill.

Thorpy, M.J. (ed). 1990. Sleep paralysis. *ICSD-International Classification of Sleep Disorders: Diagnostic and Coding Manual*. Rochester, Minn.: American Sleep Disorders Association.

Wing, Y.K., S.T. Lee, and C.N. Chen. 1994. Sleep paralysis in Chinese: Ghost oppression phenomenon in Hong Kong. *Sleep* 17(7): 609–613.

Wright, D. 1994. Initial findings of the abduction transcription project. *MUFON UFO Journal*, no. 310: 3–7 and no. 311: 3–7.

How to Make an 'Alien' for 'Autopsy'

by TREY STOKES

Much attention has been given to the "alien autopsy" film footage used in the "Alien Autopsy: Fact or Fiction?" program shown last summer on the Fox television network. (The black-and-white film footage was supposedly of a 1947 autopsy of one of three or four "aliens" whose spaceship was said to have crashed then near Roswell, New Mexico. See SI, November/December 1995.) Many people who saw the program seem to think that professional creature FX (FX is Hollywood jargon for "effects," as in "special effects") artists don't know how this could be faked. I happen to be a professional creature FX artist, so let's have a look at that particular claim.

Special Effects—The Fine Art of Fooling People

The job of a special effects artist involves: (1) Creating stuff in an attempt to fool an audience; (2) Looking at stuff other people created and trying to figure out how they did it; and (3) thinking about how we might have done that other stuff.

My opinion of the "alien autopsy"? Everything I saw in the film could have been done with modern makeup FX techniques. Many of these techniques did not exist in 1947, but my belief is that neither did this film. No theater in 1947 would have shown a film as graphic and grotesque as this, even as part of a Hollywood science fiction movie. Why would someone make a hoax the public would never see? As for another often-heard claim that this "alien corpse," if phony, would have to be the best creature effect ever put on film, well, not only do I think it's a fake, I think it could have been a much better fake.

And I, pardon the expression, am not alone. The FX artist seen on that program wasn't the only award-winning creature designer interviewed. A colleague of mine was also asked to review the footage for the program. He pronounced it bogus. For some reason his interview wasn't used. Since the broadcast, I've spoken to many other people who do this sort of work for a living. I have yet to find one who thinks the "alien autopsy" is anything other than a special effect.

Want to know how to do it? Okay, just don't tell anyone else. These are trade secrets.

A Hypothetical Example

Let's suppose I was asked to create an "alien corpse" for an autopsy scene in a movie. Let's also suppose my client doesn't want to do the "ultimate" autopsy scene—just something that will be acceptable. According to the script, the movie scene will go like this: (1) This is a period piece intended to look like a forties-era documentary; (2) The body is supposed to resemble the commonly accepted "alien" description; (3) The body will be cut open and handled by the actors; and (4) We want to show nonhuman internal organs.

None of these requirements is especially difficult. I take the job. Once the check clears, I assemble my creative team. Right away, we have some important choices to make. There are two basic techniques we could use to create the original form of our corpse: sculpt the whole thing in clay, or do a body cast. Since we're doing a humanoid character, we might choose a body cast for this job. Once we have our body cast, we can adjust it in various ways to make it more "alien." Even with our adjustments, we'll still be stuck with a mostly human-looking corpse, but the body-cast method is both easier and faster than sculpting the entire alien from scratch.

The body-cast process is essentially this: We get a live human of the approximate size we need and cover him or her with alginate, an organic product that goes on like a paste but quickly solidifies into a rubbery semisolid. (You may be familiar with the stuff—dentists use it to take tooth casts.) We reinforce the alginate with layers of plaster bandage. When we remove the hardened bandages and alginate in two big sections (front and back), we've got a "negative" of our human's body. This will be the starting point for creating our alien corpse. (Many FX companies store body casts from past projects. If we happen to have an existing body cast that fits our requirements we might skip this entire step. Now that's economical!)

If we were really in a hurry we might make our final "alien" from the body cast as is; but that could lead to cosmetic problems later. The better technique is to heat up a big batch of oil clay until it becomes liquid, pour the clay into our mold, and let it cool. Pressing cold clay directly into the mold is another option, too. When we open the mold, we have an instant "sculpture," which we can resculpt until our body is exactly the way we want it. This does require us to make another mold of the finished sculpture, but the improved results will make it worth our while. The end result of our body cast is that the "alien" will have nice muscle definition and all the subtle curves and shapes of a real body.

However, we made one mistake. (Actually we try not to make this mistake—

but this is hypothetical, remember?) We cast our human standing up because it was easier to get plaster bandages around the body that way. We forgot our corpse would eventually be seen on its back.

Unfortunately, our finished body won't have real muscles under real skin, so it won't shift and react to gravity like a real body would. This is a chubby little alien we're making—if it were real, the underside of the body would lie flatter against the table. Someone looking very closely might also notice the way the flesh appears to hang sideways, toward the toes, rather than downward toward the table. And because our body-cast subject was alive, the leg muscles will be visibly tensed rather than slack, as a dead person's would be.

Oh well, it's good enough. Let's move on.

Creepy Alien Bits

We need to give our little "alien" friend six fingers and toes—just about the easiest possible way to take a human body and make it appear less human.

We probably didn't get very good copies of the hands and feet from our orig-

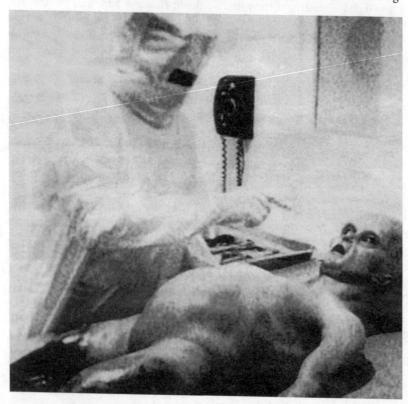

inal body cast—we were trying to get the entire body shape rather than little details like that. It's possible we didn't even include the hands and feet in our original body cast since we knew we'd be replacing them later. Also, our body cast subject was standing—if we did use the original foot position, the feet would be at right angles to the legs. We can't have that—our "alien" will look like a department store mannequin that was knocked over.

So, we make hand and foot casts of our original subject, or anyone else whose extremities are approximately the same size. We use our clay-pour technique again to get instant hand and foot sculptures that we resculpt just a bit, adding the extra fingers and toes. (An equally acceptable method would be to sculpt new hands and feet from scratch.)

We take our finished clay extremities and attach them to our clay body, taking care to position the feet in a relaxed pose. We smooth the surface of the clay over the connections, and our "alien" body sculpture is ready.

'Alien' Heads and You

When it comes to making our "alien" head we have the same options as we did with our body: free-sculpture versus a resculpted cast of a human head. Again, it's a mostly human look we're going for here, so we might start with a person's head cast. Then again we might not. It really doesn't matter either way—creating creature heads is done every day in the FX biz, whether it's to create a makeup we apply to an actor, or to create a dummy head. There are many ways to go about it, depending on the artist's preference.

To go with our chubby little body, we'd probably make a chubby little head with a double chin and bags under the eyes.

And we hope this time we won't forget our "alien" will be seen on its back.

We attach the head sculpture to the rest of the body. Now our entire "alien" sculpture is finished, with the clay skin textured throughout.

Time for the Second Mold

Because our clay model won't twitch, or breathe, or get claustrophobic, or ask to go to the bathroom, we can make a much better mold of it than we could of our original human subject. In any places where two sections of the mold come together, our "alien" body will show a seam line that will need cleaning up later. But we can be careful to construct our mold with close-fitting joints and put them in places where seams are less likely to be seen on camera.

We'd probably also use silicone rubber as the first layer of our new mold. Silicone will mirror the body's shapes and textures like alginate, but silicone won't dry and shrink like alginate does. Our new mold will last for as long as we need it, and we can refill it to make as many "alien" corpses as we want.

A Tricky Decision

Our mold will give us an "alien" that looks good on the outside; but it has to look good on the inside, too. Otherwise we could fill the mold with plaster and start an "alien" lawn-statue business.

We want a thick, wet-looking skin, lots of blood and body fluids, and a set of internal organs. And this isn't a still-photo shoot, it's a movie—so we'd like our "alien" to move in a realistic manner as well. (Yes, it's supposedly dead, but it would be nice if our "examiners" could move it around.)

It's not difficult to build a creature that moves well. It's not difficult to build a creature that can be autopsied. It *is* difficult to build a single creature that can do both. If we design our creature with movement as our main goal, the required mechanical understructure won't leave much room for the internal organs. If we design it with the autopsy in mind, its thick skin and lack of skeletal structure will prevent it from moving very well. Huge, obvious wrinkles will appear at the joints if our actors try to move the limbs on camera.

Well, it's an autopsy movie, which effectively makes our choice for us. But it's also part of our job to work with directors and actors to help show off our effects to their best advantage. Later, on the set, we'll do our best to obscure the fact our "alien" doesn't move. (If we really wanted to do a classy job we might use our mold to build two identical bodies—one to move and one to autopsy. We'd use the first in the preliminary scenes and let the "doctors" handle it all they liked, then swap the autopsy version for the later scenes. Maybe next time.)

Thick-Skinned 'Alien'

We need space inside our "alien" for the abdominal organs and brain. To do this we suspend a "core" inside our mold: a plaster blob shaped to fit neatly inside the torso and head. We place our core to allow the proper amount of air space between it and the interior surface of the mold. When we fill the mold, this air space will become the skin we cut through to get to the organs. (We don't need a core for the arms and legs; we'll just let them fill up with our skin material since we've already decided not to bother making them posable.)

We have several options for skin material. A silicone or gelatin mix will give our alien's skin a nice "fleshy" quality, if we don't mind the added expense and complexity. Foam latex, a special mixture that expands to form foam rubber, would give us a body that is soft and spongy with a semirealistic simulation of real flesh. Somewhat tricky to use, it also requires an oven large enough to bake our entire mold overnight. Polyfoam, a self-rising urethane similar to foam latex but less expensive and with no overnight baking required, is quick and cheap. And our "alien" will look quick and cheap, too, unless we're very careful!

All of these are workable solutions, subject to our budget, deadline, and personal preference. If the budget allows, we'd probably spring for the silicone skin: It cuts well, looks real, and paints easily.

Just before we close the mold and inject our chosen filling, we may want to add a bit of structure to certain areas. For example, we could embed some wire into the fingers to make them posable. (This will mean we can't move the fingers on camera.) We inject our mold with our chosen filling and wait for it to set.

Opening the Mold

We open the mold—voila! An "alien." We cut into the "alien corpse's" back and remove the core, leaving a hollow space for our "alien" guts.

The head requires a little extra attention because we want to peel back the skin and reveal a skull. We're not really going to see very much of this in our final film so all we need to do is put a solid shape—most likely made of plaster or fiberglass—into the hollow left behind by the core. In fact, we'd probably use a duplicate of our core to ensure an exact fit. If we had a bigger budget we might go as far as an articulated underskull with a hinged jaw and eyelids and so on, so our "examiner" could fiddle with the eyes and mouth during the examination. Maybe next time.

We trim and patch the body's seam lines where needed. We give our little friend a quick paint job—it doesn't have to be very detailed because we already know this dummy will only be seen in grainy black-and-white.

We stick oversized eyes in our head and put some sort of film over them. We'll be removing this covering as part of our "autopsy." It won't make a lot of sense, but it'll be icky!

We're done.

Oh, almost done. Let's tear out some of the material on the right thigh, paint a bit of blood on it, and create a big, ugly "wound." Should take an extra half hour or so.

Final Touches

We bring our body to the set. Just before filming, we reach through the opening in the corpse's back and paint the interior with blood and goo. Then we put our internal organs into place. Maybe we made some beforehand, maybe we bought some livers and kidneys at the market, or both. We seal the opening (it doesn't have to be a cosmetically perfect job—we'll never see the alien's back!) and roll the body over. A few drops of glycerin to make her eyes realistically moist, and she's ready!

Our human actors are ready, too, but first we have to give them some coaching. Because of the way we built our creature, they can't move it at all. They shouldn't attempt to raise the arms or legs, rotate the head, or shift the body. In fact, they can only touch it in the most delicate manner or it will become obvious the "flesh" is nearly solid and not semi-liquid like real flesh.

Okay, our actors are up to speed now. Let's shoot this thing.

Roll 'em!

First, we get our "establishing" shots of our critter. We have our actors move around, look at the dummy, point to it, and nod. Then we get a few shots in which they pantomime handling the creature. If they do it correctly, it won't be obvious they're barely touching it. (Not many people are aware of the way real bodies in real autopsies are twisted, turned, and flopped this way and that, so they won't realize how bizarre this "examiner" behavior is.)

While we're at it, we'll try a few close-ups where our actors very carefully move the leg and the hand slightly by gripping them firmly and moving them very slightly, just to the point where the skin would start to fold and wrinkle.

Now We Open Her Up

Now it's time to cut into the body. Here we employ one of the oldest tricks in the book. We take our scalpel and attach a small tube to the side facing away from the camera. As the actor pulls the scalpel along the dummy, we pump a bit of blood through the tube. The scalpel leaves a line of fresh blood. And if some of the blood we put inside the body leaks through the cut, that's even better!

Our next step is to pull back the skin and reveal the abdominal cavity. But first, a brief pause. Until we open the chest, we can't be sure our body interior looks properly realistic. So we tell everyone to take a break while we open the skin of the chest and "dress" the interior—adding any needed blood or details. Then we bring our actors back in and film them as they pantomime peeling the prepared skin with their cutting tools.

This leaves us with a "missing" scene between the original incision and the skin peeling already in progress. But it's a minor omission—and it covers a multitude of possible sins. After our skin-peeling scene, we can arrange our organs as needed before we roll the camera again.

Our shaky, soft-focus cinematography should help hide the fact that we're looking at a random pile of disconnected organs. Now we can get loads of film of our actors as they remove these "organs" one by one.

Let's See Some Brains

Now for our big finish we'll cut the "skull" open. We didn't spend a lot of time on our skull, but we'll do this in short takes from various bad angles so there's plenty of opportunity to adjust things as we go.

First, we use our blood-tube scalpel on the scalp. We cheat just a bit and skip the moment where the skull is first exposed to allow for any needed touchup work, then let our actors peel the scalp back. We give our actor a saw and let him grind away on the underskull for a while.

Skipping the actual removal of the skull cap, we shoot the removal of the brain from a low angle where the skull can't be seen. We throw one of our organs in there and roll camera as the organ oozes out.

And that's our big finish. Any questions?

Are you sure that's how the "autopsy" was done? Pretty sure. If not precisely the way I've described it, then something close to it.

Does this prove the film is a fake? Well, no. Although there isn't a single moment that doesn't appear to be faked, it's possible the film is genuine and all the flaws can be explained.

Which of the following is a more plausible scenario? (1) This film depicts an actual autopsy of a real "alien" whose body is constructed so exactly like a Hollywood-style creature effect that professional creature FX artists can't tell the difference; and the film itself happens to have been filmed in exactly the way a Hollywood-style scene would be shot, accidentally omitting dozens of details that would have made the film far more believable—or, (2) This film depicts a staged autopsy of a Hollywood-style creature effect.

Until better evidence comes along, I'm choosing the second option.

A Surgeon's View

Alien Autopsy's Overwhelming Lack of Credibility

by JOSEPH A. BAUER, M.D.

The remarkable aspect of the alleged Roswell alien saucer crash is that in nearly 50 years of tenacious efforts to legitimize the event by scores of believers and supposed witnesses and participants, not a single, solitary bit of tangible, credible evidence has been found to support such a fantastic and significant event. Despite the reports of extensive debris found in the field at this alleged crash site; despite the many who allegedly handled material fragments with amazing qualities; despite hearsay that the alien bodies and craft were spirited away with unheard-of government efficiency and conspiratorial secrecy to locations that remain mysterious and unproven; despite all these exceedingly unlikely occurrences, no one has surfaced with a hint of convincing, supportive evidence; not even a tiny piece of that mysterious material scattered so widely and handled by so many has surfaced for examination. Didn't anyone slip a fragment into his or her pocket? And in 1996 someone was apparently trying again to prove this was really an extraterrestrial event—this time with an alien autopsy film.

I recognize that it is far easier to create a hoax than to unmask one. But the question "Why?" effectively exposes the bizarre scenarios depicted in the autopsy film as blatant fabrications.

Why introduce a film in 1996, when alleged mortal fear of repercussions from the government supposedly silenced all witnesses for decades? If the film is authentic, why didn't someone cash in on it in a big way, decades ago, selling it to the highest bidder in a worldwide auction by an agent assuring anonymity of the source? Other than placing a period clock and telephone in the scene, why didn't the filmmaker use some rudimentary special effects to give the autopsy scenario at least the appearance of being more than the clumsy gropings of veiled, amateur actors impersonating medical investigators?

Considering that an alien autopsy would have been a unique event, the maker of this film should have attempted at least to give the appearance of the event being authentic and credible. Why not use a group of actors trained in instrument handling? Why not progress through a systematic autopsy process, rather than just slash and cut out viscera? And wouldn't it have been better to show the need to take many days or weeks to unravel and comprehend the allegedly unrecognizable, misplaced internal organs? But none of these essential procedures was observed, indicating that the autopsy was not authentic, but was contrived by low budget, poorly advised nonprofessionals.

There was no systematic progression of the autopsy, starting from a careful examination *and* penetration of organs and orifices, particularly since alien lore predicates extraordinary eyes, lack of ears or hearing, imperforated oral cavities and questionable need for gastrointestinal tracts, and no genital or anal structures. Next, skilled unroofing of the body cavities would have been followed by surgically precise and detailed dissection, delineating interrelationships, continuity, and formations of the various unknown internal organ systems, during which time decomposition of the body would need to be prevented by some preservation or embalming process. Indeed, there might have been a rare—no, *unprecedented* and *unparalleled*—opportunity to study an alien corpse; but it was not an autopsy that was needed, but rather, a systematic, lengthy, detailed, precise, anatomic dissection and microscopic study of a well-preserved body by a team of specialists of the various, presumably strange, organ systems. No less than that was done in the initial evaluations of the newly discovered Coelacanths. (When a carcass of this primitive fish, thought to be extinct, was first dredged from the depths of the Indian Ocean off Madagascar, ichthyologists worldwide were involved in its dissection, study, and preservation.)

Instead, the dramatic and graphic autopsy—performed with far less diligence and skill than a routine autopsy—was staged by the filmmaker in two scenes. First, the anonymous, hooded figures stand around ineptly trying to occupy their hands, clearly devoid of the rudimentary skills of manual examination of a body, generally expected of any physician, clinical pathologist, or other medical professional. This is followed by tentative, insecure incising, with the operator's face peering down close to the body from which he or she wants to be shielded by wearing the protective suit. Scene two shows the body open; the same inexperienced, unskilled hands are groping around randomly and unsystematically, and without efforts to recognize or analyze organ structures, relationships, or continuity. The bizarre body contents are blindly chopped out and tossed into pans. Ironically, since the external body structure appears so humanlike, the real question is, why should these internal organs be so unrecognizable?

An autopsy is done to determine a disease process, a deviation from the norm, or the cause of death. When the norm is unknown, as would be the case with an alien body, then a careful anatomic dissection is needed with frequent samples being taken for microscopic examination. Anatomical dissection consists of precise steps of delineation, tracing the continuity and relationship of

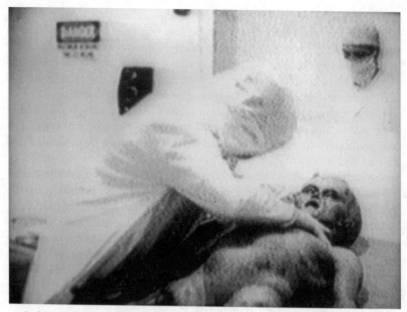

each fold, loop, or bulge to adjacent structures, particularly if the anatomy is unknown and unrecognized as claimed here.

This poorly performed autopsy may have botched a golden opportunity to learn much about this corpse. But it is consistent with an ill-designed hoax. Observation of how ineptly the instruments are held and used is also revealing, and distinguishes a skilled medical professional from an actor. Scissors, for example, are not held with the forefinger and thumb awkwardly pointing off sideways, as was done in the film. Instead, the ring finger and thumb are placed in the scissors' holes, the *middle finger stabilizes, and the index finger is used to direct the scissor tip precisely.* Dissection should be done with judicious irrigation and sponging of obscuring fluids (none was seen in the film); dissection is done with direct vision of the knife or scissor points and not by blindly cutting, as depicted. The chopping out and removal of body contents would have totally distorted the functional and structural relationships of organs and destroyed the functional anatomy.

The peculiar headgear of these hooded operators is also enigmatic. Presumably, the hoods were intended to protect against microbes, vapors, or other alien toxins. But as shown, the hoods would cause rapid asphyxia from anoxia and accumulation of exhaled carbon dioxide. Where are the pumps and hoses necessary to supply fresh air to the operators? Without a circulating air supply, the visors would also have become rapidly fogged by condensation, and vision would be obscured. The lack of a detectable air supply suggests that the hoods used for this film were sufficiently porous for air exchange to occur freely, and thus would provide no protection against toxic gases or microbial contagion. All these observations are also most consistent with an ill-designed theatrical mock-up, rather than an actual autopsy of a potentially contagious, decomposing, alien corpse.

The mode of photographic documentation also raises countless questions: Why did a professional photographer repeatedly, if not intentionally, go out of focus and usually position himself or herself behind the actors to obscure the view at the most crucial moments—such as when the cranium (head) was opened? Why was the removal of the skullcap not seen, nor the *in situ* appearance of the brain? Why was a movie camera chosen for documentation (since movie cameras were known to have a focus problem) when efficient 35 mm still cameras with close-up lenses and color film were available at the time and commonly used for medical/surgical/pathological documentation? Furthermore, why was the camera operator allowed to take away and keep a film, when, according to testimony presented, an otherwise high level of secrecy was exercised and enforced with mortal threats? Why did the camera operator not ship this roll back to the military, as he or she did with the other rolls of film, instead of notifying the military to pick it up; and why did the military—incredibly—allow the camera operator to keep this top secret film? Of course a movie camera poorly focused and poorly positioned would be the choice of someone intending to tantalize, mislead, and not reveal any information in the course of hoax.

Only two conclusions are possible from this film: Either this is the work of beginners attempting to create a hoax to resuscitate the corpse of Roswell crash lore; or, if the film is intended to portray an actual autopsy of an unusual humanoid body (a proposition untenable and entirely unsubstantiated), then it is a documentation of the crime of the millennium—the brutal butchery, devastation, and destruction of unique evidence and an unparalleled opportunity to gain some understanding about this deformed creature, regardless of its origin.

I hope that this critique will not guide someone to produce a more believable alien autopsy film.

Extraterrestrial Iconography

by JOE NICKELL

In a manner similar to the evolution of Jesus' features in art (Nickell 1988, 41–48), or of the popular likeness of Santa Claus (Flynn 1993), the concept of what alien creatures look like has undergone change over time. In the course of graduate work I did in folklore in 1982 and subsequently published (Nickell 1984), I noted (citing Stringfield 1980) that the descriptions of UFO occupants were tending to become standardized, a process that continues at present.

Consider, for example, the development beginning with the origin of the modern UFO era in 1947. (Although many alien encounters were reported prior to 1947, most of the reports were not made public until after that year, typically with great lapses in time between the alleged date of the encounter and the date of reporting [Vallee 1969, 179–90]. Therefore, there is reason to distrust the accuracy of such reports.) Several sources show the great variety of aliens described in the post-1947 era (Clark 1993; Cohen 1982; Hendry 1979; Huyghe 1996; Lorenzen and Lorenzen 1977; Mack 1994; McCampbell 1976; Sachs 1980; Stringfield 1977, 1980; Story 1980; Vallee 1969).

One notes the "little green men" reported in Italy in 1947 (Cohen 1982, 203–205); the beautiful, humanlike beings who appeared to the "contactees" of the 1950s (Story 1980, 89); the hairy dwarfs common in 1954 (Clark 1993, 177); and the many other varieties of alien beings reported in encounters down to the present. The accompanying illustration depicts a selection of such beings reportedly encountered from 1947 to the present. (Science fiction examples have not been included.) It appeared April 4, 1997, on ABC's *20/20* in a documentary on the "Alien Autopsy" hoax. There I used it to demonstrate that the aliens that were allegedly retrieved from the 1947 Roswell, New Mexico, UFO crash (actually the crash of an array of Project Mogul balloons carrying radar reflectors and instruments) were of a type not popularly imagined until many years later.

That type begins to appear in 1961, the date of the first widely reported alien abduction—the Betty and Barney Hill case. It is the little, big-headed

Alien Time Line

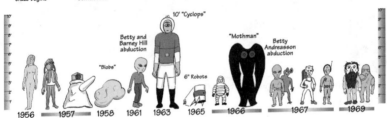

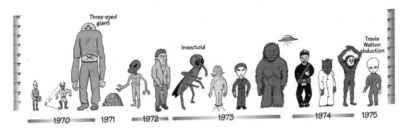

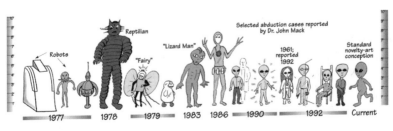

Mass-merchandise alien products showing the current alien type.

humanoid with large, wraparound eyes. The mythological implication of this type seems to be that the aliens are "time travelers"—in effect *us* as it is assumed we *will be* in our distant evolutionary future (Nickell 1984). Therefore, they have dwindling bodies (because of inactivity) and large brains (due to increased intelligence). However, some critics are skeptical of all such human/humanoid models. States one early commentator: "While it seems incredible that life does not exist elsewhere in the universe, it is equally incredible that it should resemble man" (Palmer 1951, 64).

Nevertheless, due to media influence, this is the type that eventually became standardized. It is the alien image now seen everywhere—on caps, T-shirts, ties, necklaces, posters, and books, even the coffee mug on my desk.

References

Clark, J. 1993. *Unexplained.* Detroit: Visible Ink.

Cohen, D. 1982. *The Encyclopedia of Monsters.* New York: Dorsett Press.

Flynn, T. 1993. *The Trouble with Christmas.* Buffalo, N.Y.: Prometheus Books.

Hendry, A. 1979. *The UFO Handbook.* New York: Doubleday.

Huyghe, P. 1996. *The Field Guide to Extraterrestrials.* New York: Avon Books. (I relied heavily on this source, and Vallee 1969.)

Lorenzen, C., and J. Lorenzen. 1977. *Abducted: Confrontations with Beings from Outer Space.* New York: Berkeley Medallion Books.

Mack, J. 1994. *Abduction.* New York: Ballantine.

McCampbell, J. M. 1976. *UFOLOGY: A Major Breakthrough in the Scientific Understanding of Unidentified Flying Objects.* Millbrae, Calif.: Celestial Arts.

Nickell, J. 1984. The 'Hangar 18' tales: A folkloristic approach. *Common Ground* (England), June.

————. 1988. *Inquest on the Shroud of Turin.* Updated ed. Buffalo, N.Y.: Prometheus Books.

Palmer, R. 1951. New report on the flying saucers. *Fate*, January, 63–81.

Sachs, M. 1980. *The UFO Encyclopedia.* New York: Perigree Books.

Stringfield, L. H. 1977. *Situation Red: The UFO Siege.* Garden City, N.Y.: Doubleday & Co.

————. 1980. *The UFO Crash/Retrieval Syndrome.* Seguin, Tex.: Mufon.

Story, R. D. 1980. *The Encyclopedia of UFOs.* Garden City, N.Y.: Doubleday & Co.

Vallee, J. 1969. *Passport to Magonia: From Folklore to Flying Saucers.* Chicago: Henry Regnery Co.

Acknowledgments

I am grateful to Chris Kuzniarek, *Skeptical Inquirer's* art director, for her computer-graphics assistance with the Alien Time Line.

Alien Implants
The New 'Hard Evidence'
by JOE NICKELL

Science fiction author Whitley Strieber continues to promote the notion of extraterrestrial visitations. His *Communion: A True Story* (1987) told of his own close encounter—actually what psychologist Robert A. Baker has diagnosed as "a classic, textbook description of a hypnopompic hallucination" (or "waking dream") (Baker and Nickell 1992). Now, several money-making books later, Strieber offers *Confirmation: The Hard Evidence of Aliens Among Us.* The evidence is threefold: UFO sightings *(yawn)*, close encounters *(been there, done that)*, and—the hard evidence, quite literally—alien implants!

Implants are the latest rage in UFO circles, and Strieber marshals the diagnostic, radiographic, surgical, photographic, and analytic evidence that supposedly indicates—but admittedly does not prove—extraterrestrials are implanting devices in human beings. To put Strieber's claims into perspective, we should first look at the development of the implant concept.

The notion of induced mind/body control is pervasive, with paranormal entities typically having some means of monitoring mortals as a prelude to control. Examples range from mythological beings—like Cupid, whose magical arrows infected men's hearts with love, and Morpheus, who formed sleepers' dreams—to superstitious belief in angelic guidance, demonic possession, Voodoo hexes, and zombie slaves. Folklore told of abductions to fairyland from which people returned with addled wits or sapped vitality. Popular literature brought such examples as Bram Stoker's *Dracula* (1897) and the mesmerizing Svengali in George du Maurier's *Trilby* (1894). Science fiction helped develop the alien-takeover concept, with such movies as *The Invasion of the Body Snatchers* (1956). A 1967 *Star Trek* TV episode, "Errand of Mercy," featured a "mind-sifter," a device used by the alien Klingons to probe prisoners' thoughts during interrogations (Okuda and Okuda 1997).

Meanwhile, Kenneth Arnold's 1947 "flying saucer" report touched off the modern era of UFOs and with it an evolving mythology. By the 1950s "contactees" were claiming to receive messages from the Space People. Then in 1961 came the first widely publicized abduction case, that of Betty and Barney Hill. (Their psychiatrist concluded the couple had shared their dreams rather than having had an actual experience [Klass 1974].)

With the publicizing of the Hill case—notably by John G. Fuller's *The Interrupted Journey* in 1966 and NBC television's prime-time movie "The UFO Incident" in 1975—claims of alien abductions and "medical" examinations began to proliferate. So did another phenomenon, the abduction guru: a self-styled alien researcher and often amateur hypnotist who elicits fantasy abduction tales from suitably imaginative individuals (Baker and Nickell 1992, 203).

Reports of alien implants may have begun with the alleged abduction of a Massachusetts woman, Betty Andreasson, which supposedly took place in early 1967. However, the case was not publicized widely until 1979 when Raymond E. Fowler published his book *The Andreasson Affair*. Andreasson, who seems to have had a predisposition to fantasize under hypnosis, claimed the aliens had removed an apparently implanted device, in the form of a spiked ball, by inserting a needle up her nose. Fowler speculated that the BB-size implant could have been "a monitoring device" (Fowler 1979, 191). About this time, the concept of "psychotronic technology"—i.e., mind control by means of physical devices—entered UFOlogy (Sachs 1980; 200, 262).

Andreasson's abduction report was followed by that of a Canadian woman named Dorothy Wallis. She described a similar implant under hypnosis, which seemed to explain an earlier "compulsion" to meet with the aliens (Klass 1989, 122). When we appeared together on the Canadian television talk show program *The Shirley Show* (which aired April 15, 1993), I suggested that Mrs. Wallis's story appeared to imitate Andreasson's. She countered that her abduction came first, but I observed that she did not come forward until about 1983 and that Andreasson's much earlier publication gave the latter the stronger claim (Nickell 1995; Wray 1993).

In time, David Jacobs, a historian-turned-abduction-researcher, found the Andreasson/Wallis-type implant to be stereotypical among abductee claimants.

> The object is as small as or smaller than a BB, and it is usually smooth, or has small spikes sticking out of it, or has holes in it. The function of this device is unknown: It might be a locator so that the targeted individual can be found and abducted; it might serve as a monitor of hormonal changes; it might facilitate the molecular changes needed for transport and entrance; it might facilitate communication . . . Sometimes nosebleeds occur after this procedure. Both child and adult abductees have seen physicians for nosebleed problems,

and have discovered odd holes inside their noses. [Jacobs 1992, pp. 95–96]

Alas, Jacobs relates,

> Several abductees have reported that a ball-shaped object either dropped out
> of their nose or was expelled when they blew their nose. All of these expul-
> sions happened before they knew they had been abducted; in each case they
> thought they had inexplicably inhaled something and discarded the object or
> lost it. [p.96]

Actually, one of these items did survive and was thoroughly investigated
by the Center for UFO Studies (CUFOS) in the late 1980s. Possessed by
a self-claimed abductee, the "implant" had supposedly been stuck up the
man's nostril by his extraterrestrial abductors, but was later dislodged
when he caught a cold and blew his nose. CUFOS investigator Don
Schmitt accompanied UFO historian Jerome Clark, editor of CUFOS's
journal *International UFO Reporter,* to meet the man in an Illinois restau-
rant. As Clark relates the incident, after brief exchanges, the man
unwrapped the object. "Don and I stared at it incredulously. *It was a ball
bearing.*" Despite the obvious identification, the CUFOS team sought the
man's X-rays, which "showed nothing out of the ordinary," Clark states.
Nevertheless, CUFOS went on to have the alleged implant scientifically
examined, whereupon it proved to be "an utterly ordinary terrestrial artifact" (Clark 1992).

In contrast to Jacobs's similar-but-generally-unavailable brain/nasal
implants are the current devices. The change in the situation is remarkable.
Since 1994 alleged implants have been surgically recovered but they've
become notably diverse: one looks like a shard of glass, another a "triangular" (or possibly "star-shaped") piece of metal, still another a carbon fiber,
and so on. None was located in the brain or nasal cavity, instead being
recovered from such extremities as toe, hand, shin, external ear, etc.; some
were accompanied by scars while others were not   (Linderman 1998;
Strieber 1998, 171–247).

Indeed, so varied are the implants, their sites, and other characteristics
that they recall a similar craze of yore. During the witch mania of the six-
teenth and seventeenth centuries, inquisitors identified certain "witch's
marks" which could be almost anything. As one writer explains,
"Papillomas, hemangiomas, blemishes, warts, welts, and common moles
were seized upon as authentic witch's marks, and these marks invariably
determined the destiny of the suspect" (Rachleff 1971).

Several disparate implants are described in the bestselling *Abduction:
Human Encounters with Aliens* by Harvard psychiatrist John E. Mack. For
example, two small nodules that appeared on an abductee's wrist were surgically removed and analyzed in a pathology laboratory. The lab found the

tissue unremarkable (Mack 1994, 27–28). Another implant was supposedly placed at the base of an abductee's skull. Under hypnosis the man—who believes he has an alternate identity as a humanoid named Orion—described a small, pill-shaped object with protruding wires that, he said, would make it easier for the aliens "to follow me." Astonishingly, Mack makes no mention of any subsequent attempt to locate and remove the reported implant (Mack 1994, 172).

Many of the removals have been performed by "California surgeon" Roger Leir. Actually Dr. Leir is not a physician, but a podiatrist (licensed to do minor surgery on feet). He was accompanied by an unidentified general surgeon (who did not want to be associated with UFO abduction claims). The latter performed all of the above-the-ankle surgeries.

A critic of implant claims, Dr. Virgil Priscu, a department head in an Israeli teaching hospital, observes that a foreign object can enter the body unnoticed, as during a fall, or while running barefoot in sand or grass—even as a splinter from a larger impacting object (Priscu 1998). Such foreign objects may become surrounded by a membrane, like several of the "implants" removed by Dr. Leir et al. (Lindemann 1998); depending on the material, they may also degrade over time, leaving only a small bit of "reaction" tissue in place of the foreign object—"No mystery, no 'implants,'" says Dr. Priscu. He challenged Dr. Leir's associate, a hypnotherapist named Derrel Sims, to provide specimens, or at least color slides of them, for analysis at a forensic medical institute, but reported he received no cooperation. Dr. Priscu also noted the lack of the scientific peer-review process in the case of implant claims. Although he is himself an admitted UFO believer, he states, "I also firmly believe that meticulous research by competent persons is the way to the truth" (Priscu 1998).

In *Confirmation* Whitley Strieber describes several of the implants including one removed from his own external ear by a physician. It turned out to be collagen, the substance from which cartilage is formed (Strieber 1998, 228). Strieber admits that the promised "hard evidence" provided by implants is not so hard after all: "I hope this book will not cause a rush to judgement," he writes, "with skeptics trying to prove that evidence so far retrieved is worthless while UFO believers conclude that it is proof. Both approaches are a waste of time, because the conclusive evidence has not yet been gathered" (Strieber 1998, 255).

A similar admission comes from UFOlogist David E. Pritchard, an M.I.T. physicist who, with Mack, hosted the 1992 Abduction Study Conference at M.I.T. (Pritchard emphasized that the conference was merely held there; it was *not an M.I.T. conference.*) Pritchard gave a presentation on a suspected implant, a tiny object with a collagen sheen that he acknowledged might have grown in the alleged abductee. (It had suppos-

edly been implanted in the man's penis, but worked itself out over time.)
Pritchard conceded:

> I don't have anything conclusive. What I have is just what you usually get in
> this business: it will provide more beliefs for the believers and will be instantly
> skeptified by the skeptics, and it's not very good evidence if it won't move the
> lines at all. The point is to convince the jury . . . [Bryan 1995, pp. 50–51]

Of course, it is not skeptics but implant advocates who have the burden of
proof—a burden they have emphatically failed to meet. Indeed, the implant
concept—like the larger alien abduction phenomenon itself—lacks proof that
it has an objective reality. Instead, the evidence indicates it is simply part of
an evolving UFO mythology. Its theme of entities exerting influence over
humans is one seen in many variants, ranging from ancient mythical lore to
modern science fiction and persisting in some form in popular culture. There
have always been individuals—fantasizers as well as paranoid schizophren-
ics—who have heard voices that directed or controlled them, voices that are
expressions of hopes and fears. Therefore it seems safe to predict that, as the
millennium draws near, there will be further claims of "hard evidence" of
extraterrestrial visitation. We may also expect that misperceptions and exag-
gerations of natural phenomena, as well as hoaxes, will abound.

References

Baker, Robert A., and Joe Nickell. 1992. *Missing Pieces: How to Investigate Ghosts, UFOs, Psychics, and Other Mysteries.* Buffalo, N.Y.: Prometheus Books, 227.
Bryan, C. D. B. 1995. *Close Encounters of the Fourth Kind.* New York: Knopf, 50–51.
Clark, Jerome. 1992. Abduction Artifact. *Fate* April, 19–22.
Fowler, Raymond E. 1979. *The Andreasson Affair.* Englewood Cliffs, N.J.: Prentice-Hall.
Jacobs, David. 1992. *Secret Life: Firsthand Documented Accounts of UFO Abductions.* New York: Simon & Schuster.
Klass, Philip J. 1974. *UFOs Explained.* New York: Vintage Books, 299.
———. 1989. *UFO Abductions: A Dangerous Game.* Buffalo, N.Y.: Prometheus Books.
Linderman, Debra L. 1998. Surgeon Tells First Results of Implant Analysis. Excerpted from CNI News vol. 15.8 (February 26, 1996).
Mack, John E. 1994. *Abduction: Human Encounters with Aliens.* New York: Ballantine.
Nickell, Joe. 1995. *Entities: Angels, Spirits, Demons, and Other Alien Beings.* Amherst, N.Y.: Prometheus Books, 211.
Okuda, Michael, and Denise Okuda. 1997. *The Star Trek Encyclopedia.* New York: Pocket Books, 141, 303.
Priscu, Virgil. 1998. Rebuttal to Derrell Sims the Implant Guy! Internet posting to the UFO Folklore Center.
Rachleff, Owen S. 1971. *The Occult Conceit.* Chicago: Cowles Book Co., 108.
Sachs, Margaret. 1980. *The UFO Encyclopedia.* New York: Perigee Books.
Strieber, Whitley. 1985. *Communion: A True Story.* New York: William Morrow.
———. 1998. *Confirmation: The Hard Evidence of Aliens Among Us.* New York: St. Martin's press.
Wray, Shannon. 1993. Notes of interview with Dorothy Wallis for *The Shirley Show,* n.d. (faxed to Joe Nickell March 31; show taped April 1).

Acknowledgments

I am grateful to Barry Karr and Tim Binga for research assistance, Ranjit Sandhu for manuscript preparation, and Ben Radford for reading the manuscript and making helpful suggestions.

Mars Global Surveyor Photographs 'Face on Mars'

by DAVID MORRISON

One of the curiosities of the Viking spacecraft global mapping of Mars (1976–1977) was the discovery of a strangely shaped mesa in the Cydonia region that resembled a human face. The so-called "Face on Mars" was recognized by Viking scientists and included in one of the early mission news releases. At the low resolution and oblique lighting under which the Viking image was obtained, the mile-wide mesa has an eerie Sphinx-like appearance. In the original release, the effect was heightened by the fortuitous presence of black "drop-outs" where one nostril and one eye would be, but even after proper processing to remove these artifacts, the human resemblance remained.

Unfortunately a small band of individuals decided that this formation was an artificial, carved sculpture of a human face placed on Mars hundreds of thousands of years ago. A cult grew that tried to deduce the nature of the sculpture and who made it, with links to a variety of other pseudoscience cults such as that of the "crop circles." The leader of this group was former journalist Richard Hoagland, who wrote a book, *The Monuments of Mars,* and has appeared widely on the lecture circuit and talk radio. Hoagland expanded this story to book length by linking the Face to several nearby hills in Cydonia that he said were pyramids (what else!) and a ruined city. After extensive mathematical analysis of the latitude and longitude of these features and the angles of lines connecting them, he not only deduced the date for their construction but hinted that encoded in this extraterrestrial mathematics were scientific formulas that might reveal the source of unlimited nonpolluting energy. Branching out, Hoagland later released the startling discovery that Apollo-era lunar photos depict many artifacts of extraterrestrial engineering on the Moon, including a crystal dome tens of miles high. This time the press covered the story for its humorous value only, but questions have continued to be raised for the past two decades about the possible reality of the Face itself as an artifact of intelligent life on Mars.

In addition to promoting themselves and their publications, Hoagland and

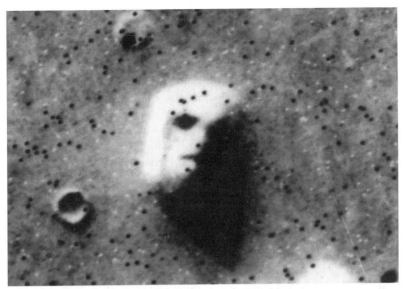

Photo 1: "Face on Mars" photo taken by the Viking 1 Orbiter, 1976–1977.

his followers developed a detailed conspiracy theory in which it was not stupidity that blinded NASA officials and planetary scientists to this evidence of advanced extraterrestrial life, but an intentional effort to deceive the public. From the beginning they accused NASA of suppressing additional Viking images of the Face, and of covering up other evidence of intelligent life on Mars while secretly planning to exploit this information. They even went so far as to picket JPL at the time of the failure of the Mars Orbiter spacecraft, which ceased to function in 1992 just before it was to begin a high-resolution orbital survey of the Red Planet as a follow-up to Viking. Stories circulated that the "failure" of Mars Observer was itself a fake, and that the real secret mission of Mars Observer was to photograph the Face.

The high-resolution Mars Orbiter Camera (MOC) was reflown on the next available mission, the Mars Global Surveyor, which arrived at Mars in 1997. Mars Surveyor is part of a NASA program to place an orbiter around Mars and a lander on its surface at every opportunity over the next decade when Earth and Mars are properly aligned (roughly once every 26 months). The first two of these Mars missions were Mars Pathfinder, which landed on the surface on July 4, 1997, and Mars Global Surveyor, which arrived a couple of months later and is now [July 1998] in the midst of a long period of adjustments leading toward its final mapping orbit. On April 5, 1998, in Orbit 220, the MOC obtained an oblique image of the Face at a resolution of 4.2 m/pixel, a factor-of-ten improvement in linear resolution over the best Viking image.

Immediately released by NASA, the new image of the Face shows a low mesa-like hill cut crossways by several roughly linear ridges and depressions, which were misidentified in the 1976 photo as the eyes and mouth of a face. The hill is surrounded by an apron of smooth eroded material that produced the effect of a halo or puffy wig in the Viking image. At high resolution, the entire Cydonia area shows much greater evidence of erosion than was evident from Viking orbital photography. Only with a large dose of imagination can any resemblance to a face be seen in the new MOC image, which is an example of how dramatically our interpretation of geology changes with large improvements in resolution. Compared to various rock formations on Earth that have a human resemblance, the Face on Mars is a pretty poor specimen, recognizable only at very low resolution.

After 20 years of promoting pseudoscientific interpretations and various conspiracy theories, will the Face on Mars cult now accept reality? Probably they will find a way out, perhaps by claiming that NASA faked the new image. Shortly after the picture was released, one caller to the Art Bell "Coast to Coast" show suggested a remarkable new interpretation to the Mars Observer failure: that as part of its secret mission the spacecraft not only photographed the Face at high resolution but then obliterated it with a nuclear bomb to destroy this artifact forever. Apparently devoted conspiracy buffs just never give up, but at least we may hope the responsible press will now drop this subject and leave it to the supermarket tabloids where it belongs.

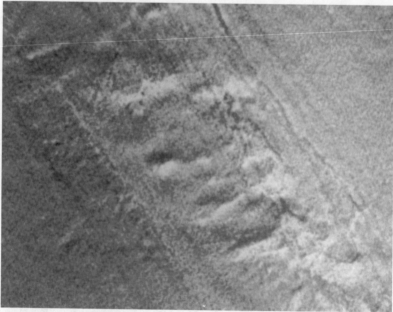

Photo 2: The same region photographed by the Mars Global Surveyor, 1998.

ENTITIES

Ghostly Photos

by JOE NICKELL

A rash of new "ghost" photographs is plaguing the Western world.

I first became aware of the mysterious phenomenon when I received a call at my office at the Center for Inquiry. It was from a Lockport, New York, couple who were experiencing some spooky occurrences and were concerned about their young children. The most unusual phenomenon, they said, was found in their color snapshots. Although they had seen nothing at the time the photos were taken, each contained strange, unusually white shapes the couple could not explain (see figures 1 and 2).

Similar pictures were taken by another couple. They had appeared with me on "The Danny Show" (where they presented UFO video sequences). Afterward, discovering I had written a book they praised, *Camera Clues: A Handbook for Photographic Investigation* (1994), they gave me some snapshots that puzzled them. Looking at them later I recognized a few that had similarities to the photos that the first couple had taken. A note on one indicated it had been made in Mexico and was similar to a photo in *Fate* magazine.

Naturally, the notation led me to the October 1995 issue of *Fate*, which featured a nationwide ghost photo contest. It was (to quote Yogi Berra) déjà vu all over again! Beginning with the Grand Prize Winner's photo, mysterious strand-like forms "infected" all six winning photos. Citing my book, *Camera Clues*, at the end, the accompanying *Fate* article explained how some of the ghost effects in the photos that the editors had received were due to such causes as film-processing errors, lens flares (caused by interreflection between lens surfaces), and outright hoaxes. What was left, they opined, were a few pictures that "may represent an ectoplasmic energy or kinetic energy often associated with the presence of a ghost; however, experts tell us that kinetic energy can be related to a living being as well" (*Fate* Ghost Contest 1995).

Yet again, the strandlike forms appear in a British photo in Jane Goldman's *The X-Files Book of the Unexplained* (1995, reviewed in *SI*, May/June 1996).

Figure 1. (above) and Figure 2. "Ghostly" forms in photos like these made by a New York State couple are becoming common.

Goldman's caption suggests the white shape is a ghost; "Or is it fogged film?" Goldman asks in a moment of doubt.

Actually it is neither. I learned the source of the ghostly phenomenon when the first young couple visited my office and, at my request, brought their camera and film for me to keep for a few days. Examination of the negatives revealed nothing remarkable, but by the next day I had the answer: the strand- or looplike form was caused by the new subcompact camera's hand strap getting in front of the lens. Since this type of camera's viewfinder does not see what the camera sees (as it does in a single-lens reflex type camera), the obtruded view goes unnoticed. Although such camera straps are typically black and photograph black (or dark) in normal light, their sheen enables them to brightly reflect the flash from the camera's self-contained flash unit.

When the cord is quite close to the lens, the result is softer, more mistlike. It follows that analogous effects could occur if other articles were placed before the lens—either deliberately or inadvertently. For example, flash-reflected hair, jewelry, articles of clothing, or the like could produce distinctive effects that might not be easily recognized.

It is instructive to note that in each of the cases I have related, including the six examples in *Fate* magazine, no one saw anything out of the ordinary but simply discovered the anomalous shapes when the photos came back from the film processors. As I point out in *Camera Clues*, that situation is a good indication that the paranormal phenomenon in question—ghost, UFO, or other entity—is really only some sort of photographic glitch caused by camera, film, processing, or other element. In this case, a new type of camera was the culprit in a rash of allegedly supernatural pictures.

References

The *Fate* Ghost Contest. 1995. *Fate,* October, pp. 42–45.

Goldman, Jane. 1995. *The X-Files Book of the Unexplained.* London: Simon & Schuster, p. 25.

Nickell, Joe. 1994. *Camera Clues: A Handbook for Photographic Investigation.* Lexington: University Press of Kentucky.

The Case of the Petrified Girl

by JOE NICKELL

Raised in the hills of eastern Kentucky, I grew up with the legend of the "petrified girl." Set in the little farming village of Ezel, near my hometown in Morgan County, the story evokes religious accounts of "incorruptible" corpses as well as ghoulish tales of the "undead."

Late in the last century—one account says "in 1880," another "the 1880s," still another "around 1900"—workmen were moving graves from the old Ezel burying ground to a new cemetery site. In some accounts the reason for the relocation is not recalled, but most state it was due to a typhoid epidemic that stemmed from the graveyard's pollution of local wells. In the course of the disinterments, the men uncovered the grave of a young girl. Some vague accounts have neither name nor age for her, while others reach near agreement that she was "a 17-year-old daughter of a Mr. and Mrs. Wheeler" or more specifically "Minnie Wheeler, a seventeen-year-old girl."

When her casket was reached it was reportedly too heavy to be lifted. But more men and ropes were obtained, and a hole was drilled in the coffin to let water out. Finally the still-heavy casket was lifted out of the grave and opened, whereupon the girl was discovered to have been petrified; even her clothing, says one narrative, had turned to stone (Nickell 1994).

Supposedly—some say because of fears the grave would be robbed and the body exhibited in a sideshow—the girl's body was reburied in an unmarked grave, the location of which was thereafter kept a secret. However, one versified account claims that the fears were actually realized: "To this day, her body had never been found, / Because her brother George sold her stone body for many crowns / to a museum for display; she brought in crowds. / People viewed her with awe in disbelief with frowns" (Plumlee 1993).

Documentation

Involving aspects of folklore analysis, historical and paranormal research, forensic pathology, and other disciplines, my investigation began with the collection of various narratives and personal interviews, then progressed to a search through the death notices in the *Hazel Green Herald.* There was no "Minnie Wheeler" listed, but there was this entry in the Wednesday, October 7, 1885, issue: "Miss Nannie Wheeler, daughter of J.W. Wheeler, of Grassy, died of flux [unnatural discharge] on last Thursday, and was buried at Ezel on Friday. Miss Wheeler was about 17 years of age." ("Last Thursday" would have meant that she died on October 1, 1885.) Federal census records revealed that "Nannie" was actually Nancy A. and that among her five siblings was a younger brother, George W. The matching surnames and the similarity of given names ("Nannie" easily being garbled into "Minnie"), together with other parallel details including the same age and a brother George, persuaded me I had found my quarry. The burial at Ezel was an especially corroborative fact, and so (I would soon learn) was the time period in question.

Further searching through back issues of the *Herald* turned up the following report, dated February 17, 1888: "The people of Ezel, feeling that the location of the grave yard [*sic*] has had much to do with the epidemic of sickness, on Wednesday commenced to remove those who are there buried to a more suitable place. We understand fifty graves will be required to accommodate the coffins removed." The following issue reported: "Ezel, Feb. 20 . . . A beautiful site has been procured for the public grave yard at this place, and the work of transferring the dead from the old to new grave yard has begun, and will continue until all are moved."

I expected next to see a report on the discovery of Nannie's "petrified" body, but, in one of the most disappointing moments in my career as an investigator, I learned there was a gap in the record—missing issues of the newspaper during the relevant period. I was therefore forced to rely on hand-me-down narratives. Although, as I have already indicated, these are quite variable as to details, the *effect* of the discovery comes through quite clearly. But was Nannie's body really *petrified?*

Petrifaction?

On the one hand, the water that was reportedly drained from the coffin could be an indication that conditions were right for petrifaction. That occurs when ground water containing dissolved mineral salts infiltrates buried organic material, replacing the decaying matter with the minerals while preserving the shape and even the cellular structure of the original material ("Petrifaction" 1986).

On the other hand, true petrifaction in the case of a coffin burial would be exceedingly unlikely. Several "petrified" people have been outright hoaxes, including the Forest City Man, shown at the World's Columbian Exposition in Chicago in 1893; the Pine River Man (made of water-lime, sand, and gravel) "discovered" in 1876; the Colorado Man (faked for P. T. Barnum at a cost of $2,000); and others, including the notorious Cardiff Giant (unearthed at Cardiff, New York in 1869) (MacDougall 1958, 23–24; Stein 1993, 13–14, 145).

Often, bodies are said to be petrified when observers are simply astonished to find them in a surprising state of preservation. For example, there is a persistent legend that the corpse of Abraham Lincoln was "petrified" and indeed had "turned to stone" when it was observed in a well-preserved state while his body was on tour after his assassination in 1865, as well as upon reburials in 1886 and 1901. On the latter occasion, his corpse was described as resembling "a statue of himself lying there." In fact, the body had been expertly embalmed and had been kept in an airtight coffin (Lewis 1929).

I researched another Morgan County case that occurred in 1921 when the body of a woman who had died elsewhere was brought home by train. When people touched her well-preserved body, it felt "hard," and several thought it was "petrified," although the railway company physician explained the body was simply embalmed—something the rural folk were relatively unfamiliar with (Nickell 1994).

In the case of young Nancy Wheeler, the excessive weight of her coffin could well have been due to its having been waterlogged (as in fact described), and/or due to the story's exaggeration over time. But what about the unusual preservation itself? It is extremely unlikely that her body was embalmed, yet after nearly thirty months it had remained free, or apparently free, of decomposition.

Although comparatively rare, there are numerous reports of "incorruptible" corpses. In more than one instance investigation has shown that the body had, in fact, been embalmed. In many other cases the body is actually mummified—i.e., desiccated—a condition that can occur naturally under certain conditions (such as being kept in sandy soil or in a dry tomb or catacombs). (It can also be induced by embalming.) Several supposedly "incorruptible" bodies of Catholic saints are revealingly described as "having brown, dry skin with the texture of leather," or being "darkened and wrinkled with age," even "completely mummified" (Cruz 1977). Some of

A relocated cemetery in Ezel, Kentucky, supposedly holds among its secrets a "petrified girl," believed buried among these graves. (Photo by Joe Nickell)

the corpses on display in glass coffins have had to be extensively repaired—for example being treated with resin and braced with wire, and even, like St. Bernadette of Lourdes, having the exposed face covered with a wax mask (Cruz 1977; Nickell 1993, 85–93).

But what about cases in which the corpse had not been kept in dry conditions but rather was found intact despite perpetually wet conditions? As forensic pathologists and anthropologists know, a body that has been submerged in water or in wet soil for a long time may form a soaplike substance called *adipocere,* which may develop in the outer layer of fat after three months or more (Spitz 1993, 38). It is estimated to become "complete in adult bodies" after "a year to a year and a half" (Gonzales et al. 1954, 68). Adipocere was once thought to be caused by the body's fat turning literally into soap; actually it is due to the decomposition of the fat into insoluble salts of fatty acids, producing a yellowish-white substance popularly known as "grave wax." It usually forms in the face and buttocks, but may affect any part of the body. Depending on the subsequent conditions, the body may eventually take on the leathery effect of mummification, or may in time decompose completely (Ubelaker and Scammell 1992; Geberth 1993). (Many of the "incorruptible" bodies of saints are only temporarily preserved and are later found to be reduced to skeletons [Nickell 1993].)

In certain European (e.g., Slavic) and other countries the discovery of a preserved corpse may provoke a bizarre response. Some people believe such preservation means the person is one of the "undead," so they may drive a wooden stake through the corpse's heart and then burn the body to end the imagined ghoulish activities of the "vampire" (Wilson and Wilson 1992).

Most likely, adipocere produced the "petrified" appearance of Nannie Wheeler's corpse which was reportedly unearthed in conditions of excessive saturation from ground water. Certainly her body does appear to have been well preserved—some say as beautiful as she had been in life, with her hands still clutching her hat. However the time between burial and disinterment had been less than two and a half years, and there have been instances of excellent preservation over much longer periods—even without apparent embalming.

An 1896 Massachusetts case may likewise be explained by adipocere formation. Reportedly, a woman's body, being relocated to another cemetery, was found to be "petrified." If it is true that (after several months) "the flowers on her breast *seemed as fresh* as on the day of her burial" (emphasis added), that is more consistent with their having been kept under cool, wet conditions than with a claim of petrifaction, since flowers that were actually petrified would have looked like stone. Significantly, there was "a spring which boiled up nearby" (Whalen 1981).

As to the story about Nannie's body being placed on display, that is probably untrue, being absent from all but one account. It was apparently based on someone having seen a body in a museum (reportedly in Cincinnati) that was thought to resemble the teenager.

It is an irony that the young lady has come to be better known for her repose in death than for her all-too-brief life, but such is the effect that mystery can have.

References

Cruz, Joan Carroll. 1977. *The Incorruptibles*. Rockford, Ill.: Tan Books and Publishers.

Geberth, Vernon J. 1993. *Practical Homicide Investigation*. Boca Raton, Fla: CRC Press, 571–572.

Gonzales, Thomas A. et al. 1954. *Legal Medicine*, second ed. New York: Appleton-Century-Crofts.

Lewis, Lloyd. 1929. *Myths After Lincoln*. Reprinted Gloucester, Mass.: Peter Smith, 1973, 259–289).

MacDougall, Curtis D. 1958. *Hoaxes*. New York: Dover.

Nickell, Joe. 1993. *Looking for a Miracle*. Buffalo, N.Y.: Prometheus Books.

———. 1994. "Historical Sketches: Petrified Girl," *Licking Valley Courier*, November 3. (Except as otherwise noted, information on this case is taken from this source, which provides more detailed documentation.)

"Petrifaction." 1986. *Encyclopedia Americana*.

Plumlee, Mary Irene. 1993. "The Major Accent" in "Poem Puts Accent on Ezel at Century's Turn," *Licking Valley Courier*, January 14.

Spitz, Werner U., ed. 1993. *Spitz and Fisher's Medicolegal Investigation of Death*, 3rd ed. Springfield, Ill.: Charles C. Thomas.

Stein, Gordon. 1993. *Encyclopedia of Hoaxes.* Detroit: Gale Research.

Ubelaker, Douglas, and Henry Scammell. 1992. *Bones: A Forensic Detective's Casebook.* New York: HarperCollins, 150–15 1.

Whalen, Dwight. 1981. "Petrified Women," *Fate,* July.

Wilson, Colin, and Damon Wilson. 1992. *Unsolved Mysteries Past and Present.* Chicago: Contemporary Books, 368–400.

Staking Claims

The Vampires of Folklore and Fiction

by PAUL BARBER

People who learn that I wrote a book on vampire lore often say, "Oh, you mean like Vlad Drakul?"

"Not actually," I tell them. "Vlad Drakul was a figure in Romanian history whose only association with the vampire lore is that Bram Stoker named the character Dracula after him. Until *Dracula* came out, no one ever associated the historical figure with the vampire lore." This has been pointed out many times, and the Romanians have often expressed their dismay over the way we have expropriated their national hero and made him into a vampire. But in the media the sensational always has an edge on the prosaic, and by being associated with vampires—even if only via fiction—Vlad Drakul has become the only figure in Romanian history that Americans have ever heard about. If the Romanians began to make movies portraying George Washington as a ghoul, we would know what they feel like.

Here we see fiction becoming "historical fact," while the scholars who try to correct the "facts" find that they have no hope of getting equal time with the people who purvey mythologies. One of these is Stephan Kaplan, who I think—but I'm never sure—is a notoriety freak who is putting us on and having a wonderful time doing it. For example, he was quoted recently as saying that vampires can come out in the daytime, they just need to wear a sunblock of 15 or higher. As wit, this ranks among the best things I've heard recently, right up there with the story that the Florida citrus industry is trying to get O. J. Simpson to change his first name to Snapple. I suspect that Kaplan will one day call a press conference, wearing a silly hat, and say, "I was just fooling, and you fell for it!" I got a call from the BBC a while back asking me for my reaction to Kaplan's announcement that Los Angeles is awash in vampires. To me this is like an adult asking me what Santa Claus brought me this year: The question had better be ironic, and the answer may as well be. So I told the interviewer that it was true that vampires are everywhere in Los Angeles, but because of the muggers they're afraid to go out at night.

The folklore of the vampire has only a slight connection with the fiction, much the way the folklore of ghosts has little to do with the movie *Ghostbusters*. Most people aren't aware that, throughout European history, there have been extensive and detailed accounts of bodies in graveyards being dug up, declared to be vampires, and killed. I took some years out of my life to study these accounts and find out what in the world could have caused people to set out to kill dead bodies. And here we encounter our first real/non-real boundary: the digging up of the bodies was unquestionably real—indeed, beyond any doubt. We know this because we have a vast array of evidence to that effect, both archaeological and documentary, including highly detailed accounts written by literate outsiders, who gave information that they could not possibly have made up. For example, unless you are a forensic pathologist, you probably don't know that decomposing bodies may undergo a process called "skin slippage," in which the epidermis flakes away from the dermis. The following account, from the eighteenth century, tells of the exhumation of a man named Peter Plogojowitz and remarks on this phenomenon: "The hair and beard—even the nails, of which the old ones had fallen away—had grown on [the corpse]; the old skin, which was somewhat whitish, had peeled away, and a new fresh one had emerged under it. . . . Not without astonishment, I saw some fresh blood in his mouth, which, according to the common observation, he had sucked from the people killed by him." When we see remarks about skin slippage, we know that the author has either (a) read a text on forensic pathology or (b) looked at, or heard about, a decomposing corpse.

Yet here we are confronted with a predicament: If our source is right about skin slippage, what are we to make of his evidence that the dead body had been drinking blood from the living? The answer, of course, is that we are not obliged to believe our informant's interpretations, let alone those of *his* informants, just because he is giving us an accurate description of a corpse. Scholars have always thrown out the observations because they didn't believe the interpretations. This is not as odd as it might seem, for often description and interpretation are run together, as in such a statement as "the body came to life and cried out when it was staked." But we'll get to that in a moment.

For now, let's slow down and look carefully at the observations in the account we have quoted:

1. "The hair and beard have grown on the corpse." Sorry, this just doesn't happen, even though many people believe it even today. It can *appear* to happen, however, because the skin may shrink back after death and make hair and beard more visible.

2. "The nails have fallen off and new ones have grown." The nails do in fact fall off as a body decomposes. The Egyptians were aware of this and dealt with it either by tying the nails to the fingers and toes or by putting metal thimbles over the tip of each finger or toe. The "new nails," according to Thomas

Noguchi, former medical examiner for Los Angeles, were probably an interpretation of the nail bed.

3. "The old skin has peeled away and new skin has emerged under it." This is skin slippage: epidermis and dermis. Many accounts remark also on the "ruddy" or "dark" color of the corpse, a phenomenon that may be caused by decomposition and a variety of other things as well. Contrary to popular belief, the face of a corpse is not necessarily pale at all, since pallor results from the blood draining from the tissues. If the person was supine when he or she died, the face of the corpse may be pale; if prone, the face may be dark. Those parts of the corpse that are lower than the rest may be gorged with blood that, having lost its oxygen, is dark and causes the skin to appear dark as well. And the parts that are under pressure—where the weight of the body is distributed—may be light in color because the (now dark) blood has been forced away from the tissues. The dark coloration resulting from the saturation of the tissues with blood is called "livor mortis" or "lividity." It is this phenomenon that allows medical examiners to determine whether a body has been moved after death: If lividity is present where it shouldn't be, or not present where it should, then the body has been moved.

4. "There is fresh blood at the mouth." The adjective "fresh" is less puzzling if we suppose that the author hasn't actually tested the blood for freshness. What he was surely observing, and confused by, was the fact that the blood was *liquid.* This was remarked on many times by people who observed such exhumations. It is simply not unusual. In fact, blood normally coagulates at death, then either remains coagulated or becomes liquid again.[1] The reason the blood migrates to the mouth is that the body, as it decomposes, bloats from the gases produced by decomposition, and this bloating puts pressure on the lungs, which are rich in blood and deteriorate early on, so that blood is forced to the mouth and nose.

And did you notice that we were just told why people believed that the dead sucked blood from the living? The standard theory about death was that it came from the dead, and when people dug up the first victim of an epidemic and found that he had blood at his mouth, they concluded that he had sucked the blood from the other people who had died. "Not without astonishment," says our author, "I saw some fresh blood in his mouth, which, according to the common observation, he had sucked from the people killed by him." Moreover, the bloating of the body was taken for evidence that it was full to bursting with the blood of its victims.

So we have cleared up an old mystery merely by paying attention to the people who, centuries ago, tried to tell us about it. From here on things will be easier: If our informants tell us that the vampire "came to life and cried out" when they drove a stake through him, we shall accept the observation and reject the conclusion: Yes, a body would "cry out" if you drove a stake into it, because doing so forces air past the glottis—but this is not because the body is still alive. Among modern medical examiners, there is remarkable agreement on both points.

Andy Tubbesing

The vampire lore did not die when people worked out forensic pathology; by that time it had become part of literature. The folkloric vampires had been peasants, but in the eighteenth century, authors were still reluctant to make peasants into major characters in stories, so the fictional vampire was moved into the upper classes. By the time of Bram Stoker's *Dracula* (1897), he had become a pallid count, rather than the ruddy peasant of the folklore. Along the way, Linnaeus named a Central American bat after the European vampire, since the bat lived on blood, and the fiction writers, noting this, added the bat to the store of their motifs. This is why, in modern movies, vampires are apt to turn into bats in the night, when they need to go somewhere quickly.

Oddly, when this material became fiction, it once again became "fact," for nowadays the media keep digging up not just scholars and pseudoscholars who talk about the folklore but also people who actually claim to *be* vampires. The scholars and the vampires are brought together by their common fate: The media trot them out every year around Halloween. The modern "vampires" derive their inspiration not from the perfectly good material from folklore, which in fact has been sadly neglected, but from the fiction, perhaps because it is more dramatic and coherent. The folklore is about cantankerous peasants who come back as spirits to torment their nearest and dearest, and this simply doesn't translate into a glamorous lifestyle. So our modern "vampires" drive hearses, cap their canine teeth, and wear cloaks when they go out at night. None of these things has anything whatever to do with the folklore of the vampire—even the canines are an artifact of the fictional tradition. Some modern "vampires" claim a taste for blood and tell stories of raids on bloodbanks and of obliging friends who let them open a vein.

The baffling part of this is that the modern "vampires" are claiming kinship not with the vampire that our ancestors actually believed in but with the *fictional* vampire derived from that one. This is like somebody claiming to be related to Rhett Butler in the movie *Gone with the Wind*. "You mean Clark Gable," you say. "No, no: Rhett Butler. You know, the character in the movie. He's my cousin." And, lacking anything further to say, you ask, "Do you and Rhett talk a lot?" But in its way, theirs is a successful lifestyle, for those of us who study the folklore have long since become accustomed to getting two minutes on television programs that then give ten minutes to a ditsy lady who sleeps in a coffin. And anyone can get media attention who will bring up Vlad Drakul or even the moribund porphyria theory, which supposes that people really *were* drinking blood to cure their rare disease, even though we have no evidence either that drinking blood would alleviate the symptoms of porphyria or that any live people were accused of drinking blood—it was always corpses. This theory never got beyond the wild hypothesis stage but has historical interest for following the trend that confuses folklore with fiction. I describe it as "moribund," but such theories seemingly never die in the media, no matter how often they are demolished by evidence and argument. By now you couldn't kill the porphyria theory with a stake.

The peculiarities of this subject have a way of compounding themselves with time. We have seen how confusing it is to have data in which accurate observation and inaccurate interpretation are all balled up together. As the discipline of anthropology formed and took shape, it looked back on its earlier indiscretions and made a firm resolution not to view other cultures as inferior to that of the anthropologist. Indeed, it took us many decades to figure out that "primitive" cultures aren't any younger than "advanced" ones. But their attempt at dispassion discouraged anthropologists from making distinctions: Now you're not supposed to notice when someone from another culture is simply wrong about something. Indeed, it's no longer politically correct to make distinctions at all between right and wrong ideas, unless of course they are the ideas of our own culture. So it doesn't bother us to say that Copernicus corrected Ptolemy, but it does bother us if I point out that nonliterate cultures typically misunderstand the events of decomposition. What is odd about our modern view is that it appears to be the very kind of patronizing that we are trying to get rid of.

One review of my book complained about my applying scientific discourse to my subject. The reviewer did not suggest an alternative mode of interpretation— intuition, perhaps? But the reason I studied this particular aspect of the folklore is that it is replete with evidence, and evidence lends itself to analysis better than hunches or intuition. One objective of the serious scholar, it seems to me, is to find likely subjects, ones where there is enough evidence to base an argument on. I have had several fruitless discussions with television directors who wanted me to tell them not just more about the vampire lore than I know, but more than can even *be* known. "What about the really early stuff?" one woman kept asking. "What about the Paleolithic?"

But we simply don't have any clear evidence from the Paleolithic. The literary evidence, going from present to past, continues to change subtly until finally you would be hard put to identify the "vampire" phenomenon at all. Early Greek views of the dead have much in common with the later vampire lore, but no one would identify Patroclus as a "vampire" simply because he appears to Achilles after his own death. And the early archaeological evidence is often ambiguous: People may put slabs of stone over graves either to keep the dead from returning or to keep animals from digging into a grave.

The fact is, no one leaves documents around explaining the things that everyone knows. It is only much later that it occurs to anyone to wonder about those things—when it is too late, and they are no longer known. So we will almost surely never know anything about the origins of the vampire lore. The most we can know is that by the eighteenth century the vampire was a certifiably dead body that was believed to retain a kind of life and had to be "killed" in order to prevent it from killing other people. And, of course, we now know that the misconceptions about the folklore have proved to be more viable than the folklore itself.

Note

1. There are other correlations here that I've dealt with in detail in a book: *Vampires, Burial, and Death: Folklore and Reality*. New Haven: Yale University Press, 1988.

Bigfoot's Screen Test

by DAVID J. DAEGLING and DANIEL O. SCHMITT

Of the varied sources of evidence invoked to support the existence of Bigfoot, none is more widely cited than the 1967 film of a large, hairy bipedal figure walking along the Bluff Creek drainage in northern California. Known as the Patterson-Gimlin film, this short motion picture (less than one minute running time) has generated considerable controversy with respect to its authenticity. The film depicts a burly figure walking deliberately away from the cameraman. The footage is often blurry due to excessive camera movement. In the most famous frame, the film subject turns its head and shoulders toward the camera to peer at its pursuer. Details of the subject's physiognomy cannot be discerned.

Recently, three independent studies have presented arguments suggesting that fabrication of the film would have been unlikely or impossible given the technology of the day. The implication, therefore, is that giant, bipedal primates have inhabited wilderness areas of the Pacific Northwest in recent times, yet have remained undiscovered by wildlife biologists and unrecognized among the mainstream scientific community.

In separate studies, Chris Murphy of Progressive Research[1] and Jeff Glickman of Photek and the North American Science Institute (NASI),[2] achieved a remarkable convergence of results when both investigators concluded, via different methods of estimation, that the film subject stood fully 7'3 1/2" (222 cm) tall. Glickman's study (1998) also concluded that the chest of the figure measured a hefty 83" in circumference and that the film subject weighed in at 1,957 pounds.

In his book *Big Footprints* (1992), Grover Krantz makes two claims with respect to the film. First, Krantz argues that no human exists whose body dimensions match those of the film subject, even given the effects of a furry costume. Second, he claims that the kinematics of the film subject are decidedly nonhuman, that the gait could not be duplicated by a person wearing a costume.

In essence, two claims seriously undermine the hypothesis that the Patterson-

Gimlin film is a hoax: (1) that the film subject's body dimensions are outside the range of human variation, and (2) that the gait of the film subject cannot be duplicated by a person.

In this report, we argue that the exact dimensions of the film subject are unknowable and that the gait of the film subject is easily reproducible by human beings of average stature. Neither of these arguments demonstrate that the subject of the film is not a Bigfoot; we simply wish to point out that recent trumpetings in cyberspace about the film's authenticity may not enjoy a solid empirical foundation.[3]

Analyzing the Claims

It is alleged that the film subject left tracks on the Bluff Creek sandbar, which were cast subsequent to filming. The tracks measured 14-1/2" in length. About ten days after the film was made, Bigfoot investigator Bob Titmus reconstructed the subject's course of travel during filming and attempted to establish the position of Roger Patterson's camera during the event. These reconstructions were performed without a measuring tape or camera[4]; quantitative efforts to map the positions of the cameraman and film the subject were made in subsequent years.[5] Thus, we know the general course of travel of the film subject but not its exact traverse (cf. Byrne 1975, Green 1981).

Murphy assesses the subject's height by taking a known quantity—subject heel width from footprint casts—and using this scalar as a calibration standard to determine film subject dimensions. Given the heel calibration and a "stoop factor" correction, he arrives at the stature of 7'3 1/2". Murphy suggests that a stick recovered from the film site years after the event is also an appropriate calibration standard because the subject ostensibly is seen stepping over this stick during the film. Using this independent criterion, he obtains the same result.

In the NASI report, Glickman employs a third method that also yields the same height for the film subject. His method involves using a later photograph from the film site of an individual of known height, purportedly standing along the original path of the film subject, as a basis from which to determine the film subject's dimensions. This calibration photograph was taken by long-time Bigfoot investigator Peter Byrne five years after the film was made, and Glickman uses the alignment of dead trees that appear in the background of the film to match the photo with the relevant film frames.

Murphy and Glickman recognize that for a calibration standard to be valid, the object used for calibration must be coplanar with the film subject,[6] such that the calibration object and subject are equidistant from the optical axis of the camera. It is also well-established that, in order to minimize error, a calibration standard must be sufficiently large relative to the object being measured. Given the uncertainty of subject position in the film, it is not clear that objects chosen for calibration purposes lie completely within the intended reference plane. The dimension to be used in calibration and the subject of interest must be positioned equidistant to the camera lens to provide accurate measurement. Thus, a scalar dimension (a known quantity with which to scale other dimensions on an object or image) measured from a calibration standard that is not exactly coincident with a reference plane, even if that standard occupies a point in that plane, will yield uncorrectable errors if this obliquity is present (i.e., the standard is not aligned with the reference plane) but its degree is not known.

For the same reason, measurement error can occur if scalar dimensions and the subject occupy a desired reference plane but when the camera's optical axis is not positioned perpendicular to that plane. This problem becomes particularly acute in the context of the Patterson-Gimlin film because camera position was not controlled relative to the subject's movements along a path defining the reference plane; thus, "coplanar" standard and subject may not be equidistant to the camera lens. Objects that are actually not coplanar may appear to be so if the camera lens is obliquely set relative to the true plane of reference.

Testing Measurement Error

To illustrate the problems posed by these sources of error, we estimated a human subject's stature from videotape recordings using calibration objects of known dimension as scalars under ideal laboratory conditions. One of us (Daegling) was filmed at a distance of 490 cm from the camera (figure 1). Three sources of calibration were used: a two-meter standard, Daegling's foot length, and his heel width. These standards were digitized on the image[7] and used to estimate Daegling's true height (194.5 cm). As expected, the two-meter standard yielded a very good estimate of stature (193.6 cm). Repeated measures within observers indicated that digitizing error was negligible, and the between-observer standard deviation was a respectable 0.44 cm. Using Daegling's foot length as a standard, the error increases markedly (204.3 cm or 3 percent above the true value). Using a heel-width calibration standard the error balloons to 28 percent (249.4 cm, with pronounced interobserver error [sd=6.5]). These figures make no allowance for camera obliquity or objects off the intended reference plane. If either of these factors are introduced, errors will increase. For example, when foot length is offset from the reference plane by 10 degrees but the length of the foot is considered to be the same as before, stature estimates are off by about 10 percent (214.9 cm). At a 20-degree offset, the overestimate is about 17 percent (227.7 cm). The degree to which the foot is out of plane cannot be reliably assessed from an image unless an independent scalar exists in the plane of reference. Ostensibly Murphy has another scalar in the stick over which the film subject steps early in the film. Not only is this calibration object relatively small, but there is also no way to verify that the long axis of the stick (the intended scalar dimension) is perpendicular to the camera lens. These observations suggest that the magnitude of error introduced in Murphy's method is unknown, is probably unacceptably large, and cannot be corrected given the known parameters of the film.

Glickman's method is far superior since the calibration standard is relatively large.[8] It is asserted that the film subject's course of travel in Figure 6 of the NASI report and the standard included in the figure (an individual at the film site) occupy the intended reference plane. The report does not specify how the coincidence of film subject and standard in this plane is verified. The calibration standard was scaled by superimposing dead trees from the background of the 1972 photograph onto the 1967 film. There may be errors associated with this superimposition, but their magnitude is not known. In any case, this alignment, however precise, does not establish that the standard and the film subject are coplanar. The likelihood exists that there are out-of-plane errors in Glickman's calculations.

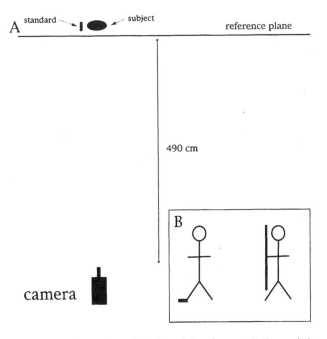

Figure 1. A. Bird's-eye view of ideal conditions for quantitative analysis. Both calibration standard and subject of interest occupy a reference plane that is situated perpendicular to the optical axis of the lens. A scalar similar in size to the subject and that occupies the greatest amount of viewing volume is preferred. Smaller scalars yield larger errors. B. The accurate estimation of a dimension (stature in this case) is dependent on the error with which a calibration standard can be measured. A 1 cm error in digitizing a standard may be tolerable in a yardstick (right), but will yield poor estimates of stature if made on a smaller object (a foot, left).

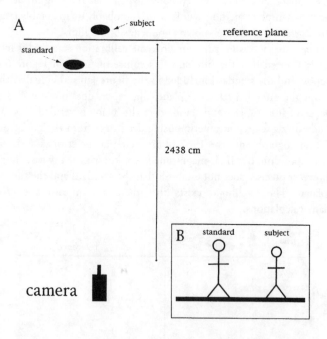

Figure 2. A. When calibration standard and subject do not occupy the same reference plane, errors in estimating subject parameters are inevitable. B. Is the standard bigger than the subject or simply out of plane? Even if the out-of-plane position of the standard can be detected, the degree to which it is removed from the reference plane cannot be evaluated from the image.

Again under ideal laboratory conditions, a subject (179 cm tall) and a calibration standard (Daegling's standing height) were filmed with the lens perpendicular to the reference plane 80 feet (2,438 cm) away (figure 2), a distance comparable to estimates of the distance of the film subject from the camera at the onset of what is regarded as the best sequence of footage. When positioned in the reference plane with the subject, the standard (Daegling) provides an excellent estimate of subject height (178.4 cm, an error below 1 percent). When the standard is out of plane by only 1 m (closer to lens) the subject's apparent height is 172.3 cm, nearly 4 percent less than the true stature. As the standard moves even closer to the camera and increasingly out of plane, the error is exacerbated; true stature is underestimated by nearly 15 percent (152.4 cm) at a position 4 m out of plane.[9]

These errors assume that the lens is positioned perpendicular to the reference plane, to satisfy the need for calibration object and subject to be positioned equidistant from the optical axis of the camera lens. The various sketches reconstructing camera and subject position in the Patterson-Gimlin film, however, suggest that the camera was only intermittently, if ever, fully perpendicular to the reference plane.[10] This would result in dissimilar distances of calibration object and film subject from the camera lens, with attendant errors in stature estimation. How serious is this problem? When we rotated the camera 5 degrees off an intended reference plane (figure 3), a calibration standard of 176 cm failed to predict Schmitt's stature of 188 cm with acceptable accuracy, even though scalar and subject were "coplanar." The apparent stature was 172 cm, fully 8 percent smaller than true stature.[11]

Glickman suggests that the error of his estimate of the film subject may be on the order of one inch (< 3 cm) although no error analysis is provided to verify this. If this error magnitude is to be accepted, the following conditions must have been met: (1) the lens was positioned perpendicular to the reference plane in which measurements were made, (2) the subject and calibration object were

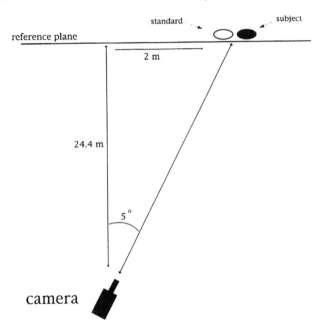

Figure 3. If the optical axis of the camera is not perpendicular to the intended reference plane, the calibration standard will not correctly estimate subject dimensions. This may also have the illusory effect of making out-of-plane objects appear coplanar (i.e., equidistant from the camera). In the example shown here, standard and subject are 60 cm apart but the standard underestimates subject stature by over 8 percent. The camera rotation requires definition of a new reference plane and repositioning of the standard for accurate estimation of subject parameters. Figure is not to scale.

both positioned in the plane of reference such that they are equidistant from the optical axis of the lens, and (3) the scalar dimension measured on the calibration object was precisely in line with the reference plane (i.e., not off-angle relative the camera lens). Published material to date does not demonstrate that these conditions apply.

Glickman's estimates of other subject parameters derived from linear measurements (specifically, chest circumference and body weight) will have errors compounded in the process of calculation. He bases his estimate of chest circumference on a formula for an ellipse that uses linear estimates of chest depth and width as minor and major axes. To reconstruct these axes, Glickman attempts to correct for out-of-plane rotation of the subject's chest. Given the uncertainty of subject position, camera position, and the lack of an accurate independent scalar in the film, it is virtually inconceivable that a mathematical correction would yield a true estimate (see Miller and Petak 1973; Noss 1967; Schmitt 1994; Chan 1997). Glickman uses an allometric equation based on living primates to calculate a body mass for the film subject of 1,957 lbs.—absurdly large unless one wishes to posit that Bigfoot is constructed of nonstandard biological tissues.[12]

Krantz's estimate of the film subject's stature is 6'6" (198 cm), well within human limits, but he argues that the chest width of the subject is incompatible with the human form: "I can confidently state that no man of that stature is built that broadly."[13] Assuming that these parameters are measured without error, this assertion may be refuted by a quick consultation of the Anthropometric Source Book (1978). Chest width is measured by Krantz in the same fashion as a distance known as "interscye" in the anthropometric literature. In a sample of 1,004 men of the German Air Force, interscye of the ninety-fifth percentile is 49.6 cm, a good 3 cm larger than Bigfoot's impossibly wide thorax. The ninety-fifth percentile stature is 187.1 cm in this group, less than 4 inches shorter than the film subject. Unless Krantz would argue that taller Air Force personnel necessarily have narrower chests, his confident statement is admirable for its faith but not its veracity.

Nonhuman Locomotion?

Bigfoot proponents have suggested that the high-velocity, flexed-hip, flexed-knee gait of the subject, which also walks with its trunk pitched slightly forward, is absolutely nontypical of human locomotion. Krantz again opines, "[J]udging from the way it walks, there is no possibility that the film subject can be a man in a fur suit."[14] Repeated viewings of the film suggest that, indeed, the subject does not exhibit the normal striding gait of human bipedalism. But humans are capable of locomotion that involves deeper flexion of the knees and hips similar to that seen in the film subject, and this type of locomotion (a "compliant gait," Alexander 1992) has been studied under controlled conditions (Yaguramaki et al. 1995; Li et al. 1996; Schmitt et al. 1996; Cook et al. 1997). Two features of the subject's gait that Krantz asserts are atypical of humans are in fact observable in humans who utilize a compliant gait: (1) reduction of vertical oscillations of the head and trunk typical of striding bipedalism, and (2) an extended period of support (weight-bearing) phase during a locomotor cycle (McMahon et al. 1987; Alexander 1992; Schmitt et al. 1996). Bigfoot investigators have also remarked upon the apparent high speed of the film subject's gait and the length of its stride as being beyond human capability.[15] When a compliant gait is employed, however, there are two measurable effects: It is possible to walk faster, and the stride length is increased (table 1). Glickman's calculated stride length for the film subject is 237 cm. This figure is easily surpassed by the authors and two other measured subjects, all of whom are less than 200 cm tall.

Table 1. Striding and Compliant Gaits

Subject	Gait type	speed (m/sec)	stride length (cm)
Daegling	striding	2.1 (0.18)	216 (7.6)
	compliant	3.1 (0.15)	293 (10.7)
Schmitt	striding	2.2 (0.34)	208 (15.9)
	compliant	3.0 (0.08)	288 (6.5)
Subject #3	striding	2.5 (0.59)	224 (53.2)
	compliant	3.8 (0.31)	338 (22.8)
Subject #4	striding	2.2 (0.14)	201 (13.1)
	compliant	2.9 (0.10)	269 (9.7)
film subject	compliant	16 fps 1.9	237–310
		18 fps 2.1	
		24 fps 2.8	

Means and standard deviations are given for N=4 (Daegling & Schmitt), N=6 (subject #3) and N=10 (subject #4) trials. Statures are 194.5 cm (Daegling), 188 cm (Schmitt), 176 cm (subject 3, and adult male), 183 cm (subject #4, another adult male), and 222 cm (film subject, Glickman's estimate). Speeds and stride lengths are calculated from forced, high-speed walks in human subjects. Stride for the film subject is given as a range of estimates (Perez 1992; Glickman 1998). Film speed is not known, so three estimates for subject velocity are given for different film speeds (D.W. Grieve, reprinted in Byrne 1975). Claims that the film subject walks too fast for a human are countered by the observation that compliant gaits can increase walking speed to match or exceed that of the film subject.

Reported stride lengths based on footprints at the film site range from 284 cm to 310 cm (Perez 1992). A human over 200 cm tall could be expected to match or exceed these higher figures using a compliant gait.

Another peculiarity of the film subject is the forward pitch of the trunk during locomotion. This is again atypical of striding bipedalism, but when humans do adopt this strange posture, a compliant gait becomes the obligate form of bipedalism (Yaguramaki et al. 1995). Assertions that the kinematics of the film subject cannot be duplicated by human agents are thus demonstrably false.

There remains the remarkable coincidence that independent studies have yielded identical results for stature of the film subject. Does this not "validate" the results in the tradition of rigorous science? Perhaps it would if Murphy's study did not involve a fudge factor in the form of a "stoop correction" the can be arbitrarily applied to the stature estimate.[16] This observation, in addition to the enormous potential for calibration errors in Murphy's study, suggests that the convergent results are most charitably regarded as a happy coincidence.

Conclusion

Bigfoot proponents have long decried the undeniable fact that detailed scientific investigation of the Patterson-Gimlin film has been lacking. There are, however, intractable difficulties involved in obtaining reliable data from image analysis where conditions are far from ideal. The potential for calibration errors in analyses of the Patterson-Gimlin film has undermined attempts to extract quantitative data from it.

Uncertainties in subject and camera positions doom quantitative analysis of this centerpiece of Bigfoot lore, as do the additional problems posed by poor image quality and artifacts of subject and camera movement. Just as measurement of film parameters and qualitative assessment of kinematics cannot demonstrate that the film subject is nonhuman, there are probably no means by which to demonstrate conclusively that the film subject represents a human agent either. Based on our analysis of gait and problems inherent in estimating subject dimensions, it is our opinion that it is not possible to evaluate the identity of the film subject with any confidence. Consequently, the Patterson-Gimlin film does not provide unequivocal proof of Bigfoot's existence, nor can the film be used to substantiate other putative images of Bigfoot (e.g., the Redwoods "playmate" video).

Acknowledgments

We owe a great debt to many individuals who provided invaluable information regarding the film and the circumstances surrounding it. First and foremost, Rene Dahinden has unfailingly given his time to provide background on the film. Michael Dennett is also thanked for his efforts in obtaining various bits of obscure but critical detail. Peter Byrne of the now-defunct Bigfoot Research Project graciously provided assistance in the early phases of this investigation. Andrew Trueblood assisted with data acquisition and analysis. Marnie Wiss provided editorial expertise and substantive criticism of earlier drafts.

Notes

1. Progressive Research is a British Columbia-based organization investigating Bigfoot evidence and marketing Bigfoot merchandise. Murphy's research results are posted on the Internet Virtual Bigfoot Conference (IVBC) established by Henry Franzoni. Readers may access the conference at www.teleport.com/-caveman/ivbc.html. These results are also summarized in *NASI News* (Vol. I).

2. Glickman is a certified forensic examiner who specializes in image enhancement and reconstruction. He has served as the executive director of the North American Science Institute (NASI), an organization dedicated to getting to the bottom of the Bigfoot phenomenon. His research results appear in "Toward a Resolution of the Bigfoot Phenomenon," a 1998 publication of the institute.

3. Chris Murphy's IVBC posting of June 9, 1997, states, "With the current findings, there is little room for doubt on the reality of the creature in the Patterson-Gimlin film. In other words, it was NOT a hoax." Similarly incautious conclusions can be found peppered throughout the various Web sites dealing with Bigfoot.

4. Rene Dahinden, personal communication, July 15, 1998. Dahinden has been involved in Bigfoot research for over forty years, and has been investigating the circumstances of the Patterson film since it was made in 1967.

5. John Green mapped the site in June 1968, Rene Dahinden did so in 1971, and Peter Byrne undertook the task in 1972. Grover Krantz used Titmus's schematic and his own analysis of the film to produce a revised diagram. The various schematics are in general agreement but differ in details of the exact path of the film subject and its relation to the camera.

6. Of course, subject and object may always be said to be coplanar, except that registration of two points does not define a *unique* plane. To establish that objects are coplanar requires registration of at least three points, or a line and a point. In the case of the Patterson film, the desired reference plane corresponds to the vertical extension of the "line" of travel of the film subject.

7. Images were digitized using Peak Performance software, Motus 4.0. Englewood, Colorado. To eliminate any of our own bias in assessing calibration errors, we used a "blind" measurement protocol. Five individuals, who were not informed of study objectives were asked to measure calibration standards. Each individual was then asked to measure subject stature for each test in a randomized design (e.g., individual I would measure stature based on individual 3's calibration, and no individual had knowledge of true values of calibration standards or subjects). Values reported in the text represent the mean value over five observations.

8. While the calibration object is of preferred size, the fact that both subject and this object are small relative to the viewing volume is less than ideal for quantitative analysis.

9. Subject height will be similarly overestimated if the standard is positioned behind the subject. Ironically, as the distance of subject and standard from the lens increases, the errors will be smaller for a given distance that they are off-plane, but they will still exist. At ever-increasing distances, however, image quality may deteriorate. This may be especially true in cases where objects are small within a film frame, as occurs throughout the Patterson-Gimlin film.

10. Schematic drawings by Krantz, Titmus, Dahinden, and Green are reproduced in *Bigfoot at Bluff Creek* by Danny Perez, 1992, Center for Bigfoot Studies, Norwalk, California.

11. With respect to conditions of the Patterson-Gimlin film, the magnitude of this source of error depends on the interactive effects of (1) the degree of obliquity of the lens' optical axis relative to the intended reference plane, (2) the distance of subject and standard from each other, and (3) the distance of each from the camera lens.

12. Assuming the film subject has a density similar to water (reasonable for most animals), one can model the subject as a water-filled cylinder and mathematically "weigh" it, with no allowance for tapering of the head or lower limbs. This procedure produces a very rough high-end estimate of

mass. Assuming Glickman's estimates are accurate, this cylinder weighs 1,625 lbs., well below the 1,957 lb. figure given in the NASI report. The nearly one-ton Bigfoot weighs nearly five times more than a large male gorilla and outweighs the heaviest polar beats by over 200kg (McDonald 1984).

13. Page 118, *Big Footprints*. It is unclear whether "that stature" to which Krantz refers is his own or the film subject's. For the subsequent argument, it scarcely matters.

14. Page 115, *Big Footprints*.

15. Rene Dahinden (personal communication and Perez 1992) reports that, on one of his numerous visits to the film site, he and others present were incapable of walking the distance reveled by the film subject in the time that it did so (assuming a film speed of 24 fps).

16. Calculation of a "stoop correction" is unnecessary in any case: one can measure body segments regardless of their orientation to one another and sum these to arrive at stature.

References

Alexander, R.M. 1992. A model of bipedal locomotion on compliant legs. *Philosophical Transactions of the Royal Society, London. B338: 189–198.*

Anthropometric Source Book 1978. NASA Reference Publication 1024. U.S. Department of Commerce, National Technical Information Service.

Byrne, P 1975. *The Search for Bigfoot: Monster, Myth, or Man.* Washington, D.C.: Acropolis Books.

Chan, L-K. 1997. Thoracic shape and shoulder biomechanics in primates. Ph.D. dissertation, Duke University.

Cook, T.M., K.P. Farrell, I.A. Carey, J.M. Gibbs, and G.E. Wiger. 1997. Effects of restricted knee flexion and walking speed on the vertical ground reaction force. *Journal of Orthopaedics and Sports Physical Therapy* 25: 236–244.

Glickman, J. 1998. *Toward a Resolution of the Bigfoot Phenomenon.* Photek Research Report. Hood River: North American Science Institute.

Green, J. 1981. *Sasquatch: The Apes Among Us* Seattle: Hancock House.

Krantz, G. 1992. *Big Footprints.* Boulder, Colorado: Johnson Books.

Li, Y, R.H. Cromptom, R.M. Alexander, M.M. Gunther, and W.J. Wang. 1996. Characteristics of ground reaction forces in normal and chimpanzee-like bipedal walking by humans. *Folia Primatologica* 66: 137–159.

McDonald, D. 1984. *The Encyclopedia of Mammals.* New York: Facts on File.

McMahon, T.A., G. Valiant, and E.C. Frederick. 1987. Groucho running. *Journal of Applied Physiology* 62: 2326–2337.

Miller, D., and K. Perak. 1973. Three dimensional cinematography. *Kinesiology* 14–17.

Noss, J. 1967. Control of photographic perspective in motion analysis. *Journal of Health, Physical Education and Recreation* 38: 81–84.

Perez, D. 1992. *Bigfoot at Bluff Creek* Norwalk: Center for BigFoot Studies.

Schmitt, D. 1994. Forelimb mechanics as a function of substrate type during quadrupedalism in two anthropoid primates. *Journal of Human Evolution.* 26: 441–457.

Schmitt, D.O., J.T Stern, Jr., and S.G. Larson. 1996. Compliant gait in humans: Implications for substrate reaction forces during australopithecine bipedalism. *American Journal of Physical Anthropology* Suppl. 22: 209.

Yaguramaki, N., S. Nishizawa, K. Adachi, and B. Endo. 1995. The relationship between posture and external force in walking. *Anthropological Sciences* 103:1 17–140.

URBAN LEGENDS

Bitter Harvest

The Organ-Snatching Urban Legends

by BENJAMIN RADFORD

The idea of having parts of one's body removed is frightening enough: no one looks forward to an amputation or surgery. Even those people who must undergo surgery do not necessarily want the affected organ or part removed, just the malady itself. The idea of having a part of the body *forcibly* taken is much more horrific. This is the basis for the organ snatching urban legend, and references to it are common. The 1978 film *Coma*, starring Michael Douglas, told a story of unethical doctors taking organs from the comatose. An episode of the television show *Law and Order* featured the theft of a kidney. Airing on April 2, 1991, it was titled "Sonata for Solo Organ." According to Barbara Mikkelson of the Urban Legends Reference Page, the show's writer said he had heard it from a friend, and the friend assured him that the story was a true account that had come from a newspaper (Mikkelson 1998).[1] More recently, a 1992 film titled *The Harvest* involved a screenwriter in Central America who uncovers a black market in kidneys. And a Brazilian film released in late 1998 titled *Central Station* featured a young boy threatened by organ snatchers. It won a Golden Bear Award for Best Film at the 1998 Berlin Film Festival and was nominated for the 1999 Oscar as best foreign language film. There is even a rock band named the Kidney Thieves.

Urban legends are becoming more common in today's society, and the Internet helps spread rumors and legends at an unprecedented rate. With the touch of a few keys, lies, rumor, conjecture, truth, fabrication, and any mix thereof can be sent to millions of people through the Internet (see, for example, Wallich 1998). The ability to correctly identify urban legends extends beyond the realm of folklorists; a modern sophistication has developed in which stories of old ladies microwaving their poodles are frequently identified as the tales that they are. But it must be remembered that, at one time, well-known urban legends were taken seriously and believed (and many are to this day, by some people). It is with this perspective that the organ-snatching legend must be examined.[2] Many people really do believe that organ-snatching does occur, just as many believe in organized Satanic conspiracies and cults. The legend has several facets and myriad roots.

Variants of the Legend

The Adult Traveler

There are several variations of the basic organ-theft urban legend. The most common one goes something like this:

> A business traveler in New Orleans takes a break from a long day and has a drink in a hotel bar. A young, attractive woman approaches him, and they flirt. They end up in his hotel room, where he soon blacks out. He wakes up the next morning in the hotel room's bathtub to find a note taped to the wall instructing him to call 911 from a nearby telephone. He does, and the 911 operator instructs him to feel for a tube protruding from his lower back. He finds one, and begins to panic. He is told to lie still, that one of his kidneys has been removed, and an ambulance is on the way. He is later told of a vicious gang of kidney thieves who sold his kidney to the highest bidder in a clandestine organ market.

In some cases the tub is filled with ice; in others the man discovers the sewn-up incision on his own, without a note or 911 telephone call. The city may be Las Vegas or New York, but is almost always in the United States (Mikkelson 1998).

The Kidnapped Child

A second type of organ-snatching urban legend involves harvesting organs from children. This legend is made all the more horrifying because the victim is not simply a randy American businessman in a bar, but a defenseless third-world child. A typical claim is that children in India, the Phillipines, and Latin America (most typically Guatemala, Honduras, and Brazil) are being kidnapped and sold to rich Americans or Europeans for their organs (Brunvand 1993). The most commonly claimed thefts are those of kidneys and corneas. Several important distinctions can be drawn between the child and adult organ-theft claims. For example,

- The traveler-wakes-up account is always told as a *story*, a narrative of how the unfortunate man got lured into the hotel and woke up with a kidney missing. The child-snatching scenario, however, is presented as a frightening *fact*. In some accounts, a police-led warehouse raid uncovers huddled, frightened children waiting to be taken, but that is about as detailed as the story gets.

• The traveler's account nearly always takes place in a U.S. city, whereas the children are invariably taken from a third-world country. This is a very important distinction, as the child kidnapping legend feeds latent anti-American sentiment throughout Latin America.

• The victim traveler is an adult man who can be said to have taken his chances by accompanying the young woman. In this view the adult kidney theft urban legend is also a morality tale of sorts about the dangers of casual sex. The victim in the child snatching is of course an innocent, defenseless child. How the kidnappers actually get the child is not part of the story because it is assumed that he or she could be easily snatched off the street.

• In the traveler's account, care is taken to preserve the man's life. In most cases, only one kidney is taken, and the incision has been professionally sewn up and prepared. The snatched child, on the other hand, is almost always presumed killed.

In the traveler's tale, the main concern is for the man who was so horribly assaulted. But the child-snatching factoid focuses more on the kidney itself and what happened to it. The fate of the child is almost incidental to the story.

Although the identities of children snatched for their kidneys are usually unknown, several children have come forth with stories of having had their corneas removed. Frequently these claimants are tracked down by newspaper or television reporters looking for a story. One famous case was that of Pedro Reggi, a boy who claimed that his corneas had been forcibly removed during his stay at the Montes de Oca mental institution in Argentina. The claim surfaced in a British/Canadian television program titled "The Body Parts Business," and was later broadcast on a French television program titled "Organ Snatchers." On November 25, 1993, four days after the original claim was broadcast, Reggi and his half-brother, Mario Barretto, went on the Argentine television program *Hora Clave* to retract the allegation. Barretto revealed that an opthamologist examined Reggi earlier that day and found that his corneas were in fact intact, but they had been damaged by disease. Subsequent investigation uncovered Reggi's medical records, which confirmed that the sight loss was due to natural causes (Leventhal 1994).

A second claim that aired on the "Body Parts Business" was that of eight-year-old Honduran Charlie Alvarado. The boy claimed that he was kidnapped by foreigners who wanted to sell his organs, but he managed to escape after four days. The documentary producers apparently felt that they had sufficient information and aired no critical examination of the boy's claims. That fell to Spiegel television in Germany, which also examined the organ theft claims, including that of Charlie Alvarado. As Todd Leventhal, formerly of the United States Information Agency (USIA), reported, "According to a June 20, 1993, Spiegel television broadcast on this subject, an investigation of Alvarado's claims by the Honduran courts 'revealed that Charlie's story was a fabrication.' Alvarado could not remember the day on which he was allegedly kidnapped, he had no bruises from the ropes with which he claimed he had been bound tightly for days, and the two foreign workers he accused of kidnapping him were released for lack of evidence" (Leventhal 1994). Despite such serious oversights, "Organ Snatchers" won France's prestigious Albert Londres journalism prize in 1995 (Barry 1995).

The "Organ Snatchers" documentary also featured a Colombian woman, Mrs. Luz Dary Vargas, who claimed that her young son Weinis Jeison had also been the victim of this horrible crime. She said that when Jeison became ill she took him to a local hospital, where his corneas were forcibly removed—a terrifying story indeed. But when the Colombian Office of Human Rights investigated the theft, the story began to unravel. In a report issued February 4, 1994, the office found that in fact Jeison had gone blind due to natural causes. In early February of 1993, the boy was hospitalized with numerous health problems including "severe bilateral eye infection," which led to complete blindness well before the allegations of cornea theft were made. The report also stated:

> The mother of the minor Weinis Jeison, Mrs. Luz Dary Vargas, received the sum of 40,000 [Colombian] pesos (about $60 U.S. dollars) from the French journalist . . . for the version of the story she gave regarding the child. . . . We note that the aforementioned journalist did not question the verbal testimony given by the humble peasant mother about the minor in question at any of the health institutions where the child was attended to . . . nor were health officials . . . or the medical records consulted either, as would have been hoped (Leventhal 1994).

A few other claimants have surfaced, but the same pattern of allegation, investigation, and subsequent repudiation is repeated. Frequently the original, alarming claim will receive international attention, but the more sober follow-up, refuting the claims, will only make local news. This leads to an availability bias problem for researchers, who are likely to overlook smaller, local stories.

Lik'ichiri: Fat Stealers of the Andes

Stories of child organ-snatching are common in Central and South America, but they are not the only tales of bodily theft. The legend of the lik'ichiri, said to haunt the altiplano (highlands) of the Andes mountains, is another. Lik'ichiri means "fat stealer" in the language of the Aymara, one of the prominent indigenous groups of the Andes. It is a well-known figure among the Quechua, Aymara, and other native Andean cultures. While in La Paz, Bolivia, in 1996, I interviewed Eulogio Chavez, an ethnolinguist at the Ethnology and Folklore museum about the *lik'ichiri*. According to Chavez, the *lik'ichiri* attacks people as they sleep on the *altiplano*, cutting long, thin slits in the victims' sides and removing their fat. The extraction is painless, and the wound promptly heals without the victim being any the wiser (Radford 1996).

While at first a *lik'ichiri* attack might appear to be a cheap and efficient method of weight loss, according to the legend the eventual results are much graver: unless treatment is given promptly, the victim will die. Treatments include the clandestine administration of a potion called *achacachi*. While the extraction of fat may seem trivial, it is important to realize that in the frigid Andean highlands fat helps keep people insulated and alive. Anyone left in the cold of the high rugged mountains without protection, including natural body fat, is indeed in real danger.

Although Chavez believes that the *lik'ichiri* is a very old belief (one originating before the Spanish Conquest in the 1530s), the urban legend has clearly been updated. Most reported attacks occur in the mountains and high plains, but people are also said to be attacked in the cities as well. In La Paz, Bolivia's capital and largest city, hapless bus riders are said to be attacked late at night. Supposedly one can avoid a *lik'ichiri* attack by traveling only during the day, avoiding walking alone at night, and eating garlic, which is supposed to dilute the fat, making it less appealing or unusable to the *lik'ichiri*.

Although some sources claim that the *lik'ichiri* is a spirit or imaginary entity, most people in I interviewed La Paz, including Mr. Chavez, believe it is a real person, or group of people, who have special skills or abilities. Such powers include the ability to put their victims to sleep and make painless, surgical incisions. Note that many of the powers ascribed to the *lik'ichiri* are not necessarily assumed to be supernatural; many people today believe that hypnosis, for example, can make others fall asleep at will, follow commands, or dull the pain of a cut. The *lik'ichiri*, then, is less of a supernatural monster than a normal person with an odd vocation. "It's not necessarily evil," Chavez notes, "but a profession. It's an economic question."

Unlike tales of native children's organs being harvested for implantation into rich foreigners' children, the *lik'ichiri* supposedly sells the fat he collects to international corporations—mostly American companies—to be used for various purposes, including plastic surgery and the development of anesthetics. According to Chavez, unscrupulous company representatives supposedly buy the fat from the *lik'ichiri* knowing that it was taken from innocent victims in the high plains. Chavez compares the situation to the history of quinine: Just as the Whites (and their companies) took quinine from the Andes and developed it for profit, the same is being done to the Andean people's life-preserving fat.[3]

Similar urban legends elsewhere in the region include the *pishtacos* and the *sacaojos* of Peru. In the case of the *sacaojos* ("eye-stealers"), rumor spread in the Peruvian capital city of Lima that bands of foreigners had taken to the streets to kidnap children, later throwing them back on the pavement with their eyes gouged out. The eyes were said to be sold overseas at a lucrative profit.

On a cultural level, the children, and by extension, the very future, of the native peoples is taken by the *lik'ichiri*. In the *lik'ichiri* urban legend, the bodies themselves of the native population are being taken from them. This fuels xenophobia, and indeed "[T]he figure of the *pishtaco* is first of all that of a foreigner. This tall white—who drinks milk and sleeps by day— goes out at night carrying under his long coat a long knife with which he cuts up Indians. He uses their fat to oil his machines and their blood to sell to blood banks" (Shakespeare 1989).

Although the *lik'ichiri* is usually thought of as a native, foreigners are occasionally accused of being *lik'ichiri* and attacked. One American woman I spoke with in La Paz who worked on the *altiplano* said she had been warned not to be seen out at dusk or night because she might be attacked by locals whose attitude is better safe than sorry concerning a *lik'ichiri* in their midst.

Despite the similarity of many motifs to the vampire legend (such as attacks that occur at night, the use of garlic to deter the predator, the draining of a bodily substance, an ability to put others to sleep and turn invisible, etc.), Chavez sees no parallels between the two: "One is fiction," he said. "The other occurs right here."

The Organ Trade in China and India

It would be naive to believe that there is no organ *commerce* in the world at all. There are many verified cases of organ selling; indeed, in some countries selling one's organs is perfectly legal. In the United States, it is against the law, although some have suggested that legalizing it would save lives and be beneficial to all involved.

In India, for example, some adults voluntarily sell one of their kidneys. Although the sale of of kidneys is seen by many in the United States as morally objectionable, it should be remembered that in India, as in many developing countries, sophisticated medical equipment is rare and in many cases the resources simply are not available to extract and preserve organs of those killed in accidents for later transplant. Few Indians who suffer from kidney failure can afford dialysis treatments, so they can either die or purchase a kidney. In 1994, the Indian parliament passed a law making it illegal to buy or sell human organs for transplantation, but "A loophole in the law allows people who are related to the recipient only by ties of affection to donate organs with committee approval" (Cohen 1998).[4]

One case of organ selling that made headlines in 1989 was that of Ahmet Koc, a Turk who traveled to Britain to sell one of his kidneys. In December of 1989, Koc claimed that three months before, he had been brought to Britain with the promise of a job. When he went in for a medical check, he was given an injection that he believed to be a blood test, but woke up the next day to find that a kidney had been removed. He was told not to be upset, because he would be well paid for his loss.

It was later revealed that Mr. Koc was in fact one of four Turks who voluntarily sold their kidneys that day in September of 1988. He was apparently unhappy with the amount paid him, and went to the press with his story. Although transplanting brokered kidneys was legal at the time in Britain, three London doctors who participated in the transplant were found guilty of professional misconduct. The law has since been changed, presumably in large part due to the furor over the Koc case. Again, as frequently occurs, the original, bizarre claims received enormous publicity while the truth about Koc came only much later and was barely reported or noticed. It is likely that the Koc case did much to spawn the urban legend of adult organ snatching.

Organs taken from recently executed Chinese prisoners is another example. Although the Chinese government claims that such organ harvesting is rarely done and then only with the consent of the prisoners, several respected human rights organizations insist otherwise. A 1994 Human Rights Watch/Asia report documented proof that some condemned prisoners are killed and their organs taken from them immediately after the execution. It further concludes that executed prisoners are the "principal source" for transplant organs in China (Leventhal, 1994); a similar conclusion was reached by Amnesty International.

The Urban Legend Gains Credibility

The organ-snatching legend reached a peak of popularity in the mid-1990s, when several prominent organizations gave the rumors credibility. As noted earlier, several media outlets ran stories about child organ trafficking, including the Brazilian newspaper *Correio Braziliense* and a book published in Spain titled *Niños de Repuesto* ("Spare-Parts Children").

Further credibility was lent when the World Organization Against Torture issued a report by its director, Eric Sottas, in March of 1994. The paper, titled "Trade in Organs and Torture," listed six Latin American countries as confirmed traffickers in child organs. Sottas rehashed numerous accounts, many of them long since disproven, of organ trafficking. Sottas included, for example, the case of Pedro Reggi, the Argentine boy mentioned earlier who had lost his sight to disease, not cornea thieves (Sottas 1994).

The child organ-snatching legend even made it to the European Parliament. As Leventhal (1994) notes, the European Parliament adopted a "Resolution on Prohibiting Trade in Transplant Organs" on September 14, 1993. The resolution "calls for action to be taken to put a stop to the mutilation and murder of foetuses, children, and adults in certain developing countries for the purpose of providing transplant organs." The resolution was based on a report submitted by special rapporteur Leon Schwartzenberg, a former Minister of Health of France. Schwartzenberg's report was credulous of the organ-snatching legends, and the author based his conclusions on many dubious and recanted sources.

Rafael Matesanz, national coordinator for transplants of Spain's National Organization for Transplants, prepared a report in response to the resolution in which he stated: "The reference to [rumors of child organ trafficking] in an official document controlled by the European Parliament is improper from any standpoint, because it implies acknowledgement that such practices exist . . ." (quoted in Leventhal 1994).

Dubious Claims

With many and varied reports and rumors, as well as claimants to the organ-snatching urban legend, the myth seems reasonable to many people. After all, bizarre things happen all the time; why couldn't this be true?

The short answer is that, like all urban legends, yes, it could be true. It could be that at some point a little old lady really microwaved her poodle. And it is not technically impossible that giant alligators could roam the sewers of New York. But the evidence for organ snatching, just like the evidence for most urban legends, is simply not there. Because extraordinary claims require extraordinary evidence, the onus is on those claiming that such a trade is in fact occurring. As yet, the evidence has fallen far short of the mark. To the contrary, many factors make organ-snatching claims suspect.

To begin with, it would be nearly impossible to conceal an entire organ-snatching ring. Kidney transplants are not simple procedures that can be done in someone's kitchen. Sophisticated medical equipment must be used, and donors and recipients must be carefully matched. Blood and tissue typing and histocompatibility tests must be done in advance. The operation would take between four and six hours and involve ten to twenty support staff, including three members of a surgical team, an anaesthesiologist, and two nurses. It would be a practical impossibility to assemble a large team of highly trained medical personnel willing to engage in such illegal and unethical behavior. Highly paid medical staff here and abroad are unlikely to risk performing such operations, placing both their licenses and their reputations in jeopardy.

Dangers of Legends

The detrimental effects of the organ-snatching urban legend are manifold. Fear that organs are being forcibly taken from unsuspecting people decreases organ donations. For example, in the Cordobá region of Argentina, organ donations dropped 90 percent after Pedro Reggi's claims of cornea snatching circulated. And, according to Leventhal (1994), "After false charges of cornea theft in Colombia were publicized in a French television program in November 1993, cornea donations in Colombia plummeted, decreasing by 90 percent, according to the Pan-American Association of Eye Banks. Prior to the false charges, cornea donations in Colombia averaged 94 per month, but dropped to eight to ten per month after the program." This sort of public reaction costs people's lives, particularly in cases of kidneys and other organs. Every kidney, cornea, or other organ not donated is one less that could help someone to see or live another year.

In many poor areas, such as in the slums of Brazil, residents may avoid treatment in public hospitals out of fear that their organs may be taken (Scheper-Hughes 1998). The results can be tragic, since the poor are frequently those who need medical services the most.

The United Network for Organ Sharing issued a position statement on February 21, 1997, titled, "Debunking the Kidney Heist Hoax," which reads in part, "There is absolutely no evidence of such activity ever occurring in the U.S. . . . but it is possible that some believe it and decide against organ donation out of needless fear." The National Kidney Foundation, in an effort to dispel the rumor, has asked that anyone who claims to have been a victim of illegal kidney theft to step forward and contact the foundation. No one has yet presented a confirmable case in which a child or adult was kidnapped and his or her organs taken.

On December 29, 1998, Howard Nathan, executive director of the Delaware Valley Transplant Program, issued a plea for "Internet users to make New Year's resolutions not to forward false e-mail messages about a supposed organ snatching scheme." In a press release he stated, "The Internet story continues to be circulated and has a negative and harmful impact on the public's perception of the medical community and the organ donor program. . . . We shouldn't have to compete with false and outrageous organ donation stories on the Internet or anywhere else."

Inter-country adoptions suffer as well. Thousands of children who would otherwise be adopted by loving American or European families remain in orphanages throughout South America. Local adoption agencies are nervous about incurring their communities' wrath and suspicions that they are in collusion with traffickers of babies and baby organs.

While a decrease in organ donations may kill people indirectly, even worse can happen when unsubstantiated rumors spread and are acted upon. Unprovoked attacks on foreigners have occurred, many in the mid-1990s. In March of 1994, Melissa Larson, a woman from New Mexico, was hiking in Guatemala when she was taken to jail for routine questioning. Rumors quickly spread in the town of Santa Lucia Cotzumalguapa that she was detained for selling babies and baby organs. When she was transferred to a larger jail, townspeople rioted, believing that she had bribed guards to be let free. The riot left sixty people hospitalized and led to fifty arrests (Morello 1994).

The following month, Alaska native June Weinstock was beaten unconscious and stabbed by a mob of about 300 angry villagers in western Guatemala. The 52-year-old woman suffered multiple stab wounds, three skull fractures, a broken arm, and a broken leg. She fell into a coma shortly thereafter and, as of 1994, had recovered from the coma but remained severely impaired. Weinstock was accused of abducting an eight-year-old boy who was actually at a religious procession and later returned home (Canto 1994).

In a letter to a travel magazine, James Sleeman of the U.K. writes, "[In Peru] we met Indians from the village where two Americans had stopped and been shot in 1995. The Aguaruna are very superstitious and most believe in mythical bogeymen called 'pishtacos' . . . The Americans apparently were travelling by raft and decided to camp at dusk on an island which they did not realize was near a village; the locals panicked and shot them" (Sleeman 1997; for a fuller account, see Cahill 1995).

Despite the dangers of such rumors, the allegations still circulate. In July 1998, Mexican Cardinal Juan Sandoval Iñiguez was quoted in *El Informador*, a leading Guadalajara daily newspaper, as saying that 20,000 Mexican children have been snatched and transported abroad so that their vital organs could be harvested. The cardinal failed to provide any evidence of his assertion or to name which country he believed was importing the children (Forbes 1998). And as of late 1998, Brazilian police reportedly suspect body parts theft in the cases of seven disappearances in the Amazon.

It is important to remember that urban legends are not necessarily harmless, and in fact can cause serious harm to innocent people. Rumors, urban legends, and misinformation can easily lead to disaster, and it serves us all to subject them to skeptical inquiry.

Acknowledgments

I would like to express my appreciation to Jan Harold Brunvand and Joe Nickell for their helpful comments and suggestions on this paper, and to Center for Inquiry librarian Tim Binga for his research help.

Notes

1. This sort of report is quite common, particularly in the spread of urban legends. The term for the phenomenon is "source amnesia." It occurs because factual information is apparently stored in a different part of the brain than the source of that information. So while the information itself is retained, the source may be misremembered or lost, and of course the source is essential for determining the credibility of the information.

2. Some of the body parts mentioned here, such as corneas, fat, and eyes, are not organs. The distinction is important because corneas, as nonvascular tissue, need not be implanted in a recipient immediately. They remain viable for between one and two weeks, while a kidney must be implanted within approximately two days. Because of this, claims that kidneys are taken from rural areas and shipped to Europe, for example, are highly suspect; the kidneys would likely be unusable when they arrived. In the case of fat theft, the usual reason for the harvesting is not transplanting, so such considerations are not applicable.

3. Quinine is a medicinal compound derived from the bark of the cinchona tree, native to the Andes. The drug is effective against malaria, heart disease, and other ailments. It was used to treat malaria in Peru as early as 1638. Quinine was introduced to Europe in 1640, where demand for the drug eventually threatened native Peruvian forests. As frequently occurs when natural medicines are discovered by the West, many indigenous people feel that their resources have been exploited, and that they have received nothing in return for their valuable medicinal knowledge.

4. There have been unconfirmed reports of poor, illiterate Indians in Bangalore who were duped into being anesthetized only to discover that a kidney had been removed. While such stories are possible, they are doubtful for the same reasons described later in this article.

References

Barry, John, and David Schrieberg. 1995. Too Good to Check. *Newsweek*, June 26.

Brooks, Alison. 1993. Frankenstein stalks the urban jungle. *New Scientist* 23 January.

Brunvand, Jan Harold. 1993. *The Baby Train and Other Lusty Legends*. New York: W.W. Norton.

Cahill, Tim. 1995. A darkness on the river. *Outside* magazine, November.

Campion-Vincent, Veronique. 1990. *The Baby-Parts story: A new Latin American legend*. Western Folklore 49:9–25.

Canto, Minerva. 1994. Rumors nearly killed N.M. traveler. *Albuquerque Journal* 17 April.

Chavez, Eulogio. 1996. Personal interview with the author.

Cohen, Lawrence. 1998. Quoted in Scheper-Hughes, Nancy.

Forbes, Michael. 1998. Cardinal helps spread child organ-trafficking myth. *Colony Guadalajara Reporter* 4 July.

Ferreri, Eric. 1998. Urban legends pick up steam on the Internet. *Buffalo News*, 15 April.

Kidney-napping: India's Organ Thieves. 1995. *Details*. June, p. 36. (No author cited).

Leventhal, Todd. 1994. The child organ trafficking rumor: A modern "urban legend." *U.S. Information Agency Report to the United Nations Special Rapporteur*. Washington D.C.: U.S. Information Agency.

Mikkelson, Barbara and David P. Mikkelson. 1998. You've got to be kidneying. Urban legends reference page. Web site: http: snopes.simplenet.com.

———. 1998b. Personal correspondence.

Morello, Carol. 1994. Baby theft panic cools Guatemalan tourism, adoptions. *Albuquerque Journal* 17 April.

Orlebar, Edward. 1994. Guatemalan army may be fueling fire. *Albuquerque Journal* 3 January.

Radford, Benjamin. 1996. Lik'ichiri: menace or myth? *Bolivian Times* 9 May.

Scheper-Hughes, Nancy. 1998. Truth and rumor on the organ trail. *Natural History* October.

Schramm, Raimund. 1988. Monstruos dormidos, heroes cuturales y plantas en crecimiento. *Bibiloteca Ethnologia.* Boliviana: Cochabamba.

Shakespeare. 1989. Quoted in Campion-Vincent 1990.

Sifuentes, Eudosio. 1989. La continuidad de la historia de los pishtacos en los "robaojos" de hoy. In *Pishtacos de verdugos a sacaojos.* Juan Ansion, Ed. Tarea, Asociacion de Publicaciones Educativas: Lima. Peru.

Sleeman, James. 1997. Untitled letter to magazine. *Planet Talk* October-December.

Sottas, Eric. 1994. *Trade in organs and torture.* Presentation and report for Eurosciences Media Workshop. Geneva, Switzerland: World Organization Against Torture.

Velasquez, Zenobio Calizaya. 1994. Liquichiris y k'arisiris su relacion con los pueblos pre-aymaras. In *Educacion Bilingue E Intercultural Reunion Anual de Etnologia 1994.* Tomo 1. Museo Nacional de Etnologia y Folklore: Lima, Peru.

Wallich, Paul. 1998. This is not a hoax! (Cyber View column) *Scientific American* November.

Gray Barker

The 'Men In Black' Myth-Maker

by JOHN C. SHERWOOD

If Gray Barker were alive today, he'd think he'd died and gone to heaven. Seems that now everyone has heard of the "Men in Black," a concept he first raised to prominence in UFO lore.

And, of course, he'd try to make a fast buck off of them.

The late Gray Barker, head of Saucerian Publications and author of numerous books about flying saucers, was one of the most prolific writers and publishers in the "fringe" area of UFO fanaticism.

Some amusing yet disturbing details about Barker's constructive (and certainly destructive) contributions to the fantasy world of UFOs have lurked in my files for decades. Despite the personal shame I attach to them, their general release is long overdue.

Gray and I never met face to face, but I owe to him the beginning of my journalistic career, and my only corrupt journalistic experience. In 1967, he published my somewhat juvenile "history" of the 1966 Michigan UFO "scare," a book Gray titled *Flying Saucers Are Watching You*. Its publication gained me my first newspaper job. After that, Gray and I shared a lengthy correspondence, and he may even have considered me one of his protégés. Gray also put me in touch with some of the more extravagant figures in the UFO field, including the notorious Richard Shaver of "Shaver mystery" fame, and enjoyed my reciprocal sense of humor.

I pulled Gray's letters out of my files after my wife and I saw the trailer for the 1997 summer movie hit *Men in Black*, the Tommy Lee Jones/Will Smith megamillion-dollar movie spectacle that owes a fair share of its style to Gray's 1956 book *They Knew Too Much about Flying Saucers*. The fact that I had kept the letters might bother Gray now, considering what I'm about to confess. In fact, Gray (and some others deceived by what he and I concocted) may meet me in hell with fangs at the ready. To those who were fooled, I certainly owe an apology for the role I played. But it's time that this material was made public.

Barker's day job was as a theatrical film booker in Clarksburg, West Virginia. He also was a talented writer, an early lover of flying-saucer lore, and a man who could make a good story better. He was hyperimaginative and could have written science fiction.

A lot of what he wrote probably was just that. But he always offered his accounts as fact.

They Knew Too Much about Flying Saucers made the Men in Black (M.I.B.) feared within UFO circles during the late 1950s and 1960s. The book now is hard to find, and my hardcover copy—the third printing—has crispy pages. In it, Gray told about alleged brushes between the sinister M.I.B. and a Connecticut man, Al K. Bender, who set the pace for what is now the stereotypical M.I.B. story: Someone sees a UFO and tries to tell the world about it. Without warning, three men in black suits and driving a big black car confront the witness. Afterwards, the witness appears too frightened to talk further about the UFO—or anything else. *Woo-WOOO-oo!*

In account after account within the pages of *They Knew Too Much* and subsequent writings by others (including John Keel, who began using the shorthand "M.I.B." in his writings), the mysterious trio—who at times seem to have uncanny mental powers and weird, otherworldly faces—squelch all discussion about supposedly true UFO encounters. The whole notion smacked of a huge, pre-Watergate conspiracy.

As I began to write this apologetic revelation in July 1997, the news came that the U.S. Central Intelligence Agency indeed may have participated in a coverup not unlike that supposedly initiated by the fabled M.I.B. U.S. intelligence historian Gerald K. Haines. He wrote an unclassified article for *Studies of Intelligence*, a CIA journal, revealing that during the 1950s the U.S. Air Force and other agencies actually did conspire to suppress the UFO issue and to concoct false cover stories to explain sightings of such super-secret U.S. spy planes as the U-2 and later the SR-71 Blackbird (the Internet address for Haines's study is www.odci.gov/csi/studies/97unclas/ufo.html).

So, Bender, Barker, and the rest indeed may have been inspired by a grain (or several grains) of truth. But that doesn't contradict what I am about to disclose about Barker's participation in—and encouragement of—actual fraud to perpetuate sales of his UFO books and magazines.

I knew little about the bizarre world of "UFOlogy" when I typed up a detailed account about the 1966 Michigan UFO sightings and sent the manuscript to Saucerian Publications, the book company Gray had set up with the profits from *They Knew Too Much*. Gray published my book in 1967, paid me a satisfying sum, and made me a published writer at age seventeen. With that on my resume, I got my first newspaper job, in my hometown of Marshall, Michigan. Two years later, I was working in the *Battle Creek Enquirer* newsroom in Battle Creek, Michigan, where I work as opinion-page editor today.

Meanwhile, Gray and I continued to correspond. Here's one telling excerpt from a letter of his dated June 27, 1968: "Strictly off the record, unusual interest and fixation upon UFOs represents, in my opinion, a definite symptom of neurosis. . . . I cannot (again off the record) bear for very long most of the people and the fans of saucerdom, mainly because most of them are oral aggressors (i.e., they talk all the time about saucers and make you listen). I do genuinely like a few saucerers (and former saucerers) like yourself, who, along with their interest in saucers, seem to be pretty sane and can have a sense of humor about it."

That same year, in creative zeal, I had sent to him a sci-fi piece I wrote about a scientific organization that discovers that UFOs are actually time machines, then encounters a more sinister enemy group of time-travelers who try to destroy them. The story began with a pseudoscholarly discussion by a fictitious scientist, Dr. Richard H. Pratt, about time travel and UFOs. The rest of it was about Pratt's mysterious encounter with three strange individuals "trapped" in our own time.

Gray urged me to try to make the incident seem real by creating a fictitious organization out of whole cloth. In youthful amorality, I picked up Gray's ball and sent a letter to Ray Palmer's *Flying Saucer* magazine, which, in early 1969, published verbatim my anonymous announcement of the formation of an organization that identified itself only as the B.I.C.R., supposedly formed by three men whose names were given as William A. Gautier, Thomas Harper, and R. James Kipling (names I concocted using my shelf of books by great fiction writers). Meanwhile, as I prepared for my busy college years, I had disbanded a small but legitimate UFO-investigation group I had led since 1965 and ceased publishing a small "saucer 'zine" I had been sending to associates in thirteen states.

Gray's letter quoted above went on about the reaction to the news in the UFO world about my UFO group's disbandment: "Did you see *Saucer Scoop?*" he wrote. "They're doing a big deal on you, suggesting you really were hushed by the blackmen. I'll always be glad to print an article by you if you'll tell the *real* (or made up) story of how these strange forces made you quit. You might as well go out of saucers in the usual syndrome."

I wrote to Gray saying that I would follow up in the form of a rewritten version of the Dr. Pratt/time-travel sci-fi piece I'd already sent him. I said I would make it clear that it was just a story. Here was his response on July 12, 1968: "I think that the sci-fi story you are thinking of, revealing at the end that it's made up, would be a little too negative. Already some readers are accusing us of making up things (which we *do* occasionally of course). How about an article just making your exiting from research even *more* mysterious than ever!"

In my youthful naiveté and desire to be published, I didn't challenge the wrongness of this. It took me a few months to put together the revised story, now ready to be published as true. In a letter dated December 7, 1968, Gray coached me: "Try to make it as technical as possible to make it look like a real scientific report. The real scientists who read our 'zine will see the hoax and I hope take it as a joke." My article "Flying Saucers: Time Machines," by "Dr. Richard H. Pratt," was published in the Spring/Summer 1969 issue of Barker's magazine *Saucer News*, followed by "The Strange B.I.C.R. Affair" in the Summer 1970 issue.

An interim letter, recounting his work on a book about the West Virginia "Mothman" sightings, reflects Gray's attitude about publishing fiction as nonfiction: "About half of it is a recounting of actual sightings and events in the Ohio Valley circa 1966. . . . I think that the 'true accounts' are told in an exciting way, but I have deliberately stuck in fictional chapters based roughly on cases I had heard about." Evidently, Gray had few qualms about publishing as fact fictional material deliberately contrived for release under the Saucerian Press label and for *Saucer News*.

Gray wrote to me about the reaction to "Flying Saucers: Time Machines": "Evidently the fans swallowed this one with a gulp." Subsequent notes in my files include copies of letters Gray sent to other UFO researchers, including Ray Palmer, disingenuously requesting follow-up data on the supposedly true identity of "Richard H. Pratt," who now supposedly had dropped mysteriously from sight. These notes thankfully drew suspicion away from myself.

In early 1983, shortly before he died of a heart attack, Gray published another book, *M.I.B: The Secret Terror Among Us*, which he dedicated to Al K. Bender, the Connecticut man who had inspired *They Knew Too Much*. Gray devoted an entire chapter to "Dr. Pratt" and presented the story as if it really might be true. To my perpetual shame, I shut up again. After all, I told myself, Gray had given me my career break—and he was publishing my stuff. I tried to ignore that he was playing fast and loose with the truth. And I had realized that a lot of what he had written before probably was just as loose.

Over the years, I have received mail from various people who have wondered whether I might know something about the background of the strange "B.I.C.R. affair." I always claimed that I knew nothing or that I didn't want to talk more about it. Even after Gray died, I kept quiet.

But the myth has moved to a new stage in its evolution, and it is only right that some background be provided about the man who helped to launch it. I have tuned in the TV series *Night Skies* and seen the Men in Black portrayed as government agents flying scary black helicopters. And, of course, it wouldn't surprise me to see Tommy Lee Jones and Will Smith return in a sequel to the blockbuster movie hit. It's only a matter of time before someone puts together a supposed "true history" of the M.I.B.; and because of Gray, it will be very difficult to separate the wheat (if there is any) from the chaff.

The saving grace is that the movie was presented as a comedy. That's appropriate, because so much of it really is a huge joke. And that weird laughter you hear is coming from Gray Barker's grave.

"Lights Out!"

A Faxlore Phenomenon

by JAN HAROLD BRUNVAND

On Saturday August 14, 1993, a small news item—about six column inches—debunking a "faxed warning about gang initiation," appeared in the *Memphis Commercial Appeal.* The headline was "Officials Deny Faxing Gang Warnings," and the subhead read, "Untrue documents promote hysteria." The documents were described as "heavily faxed" and claimed to be official police bulletins. They stated, "This is the time of year for gang initiation," and described the specific threat as follows:

> One of the methods used this year will be for gang members to drive with their lights off at night. When you blink your lights or flash your high beams, they will follow you home and attempt to murder you.

At a press conference, officials of Memphis and of Shelby County, Tennessee, said that these "fax driven rumors criss-crossed the county this week," that police were inundated with calls about them, but that no local law-enforcement office had sent out the faxes, nor was there any evidence for such gang initiation practices.

Although it is clear in this news item that the "Lights Out!" rumor was already in active circulation, this is the earliest example I have located. The next time I encountered the rumor was in an e-mail message from Chicago sent on September 9, and the next *published* report I found was in a suburban Chicago newspaper on September 11, four weeks after the Memphis report. But soon the "Lights Out!" rumor emerged in many cities and became a matter of national concern. The flap continued through autumn 1993 and even into the new year in some places. The rumor was driven nationwide largely by facsimile transmissions and thus provides a unique example of a faxlore phenomenon, likely the trend of the future in the circulation of urban rumors and legends.

I collected three kinds of information about "Lights Out!": (1) copies of the warnings themselves, (2) letters from people reporting on the warnings, and (3) further news stories.

My September 9 e-mail report came from someone at the University of Chicago who forwarded a memo credited to the Security Division of the First National Bank of Chicago. The first line, "Beware," was followed by two exclamation points; the capsule description of the initiation ritual, said to be planned for "the Chicagoland area," was followed by the bare elements of an illustrative story: "To date, two families have already fallen victim to this senseless crime." The memo concluded with an appeal for readers to "inform your friends and family not to flash their car lights at anyone!" This early example of the "Lights Out!" warning displays typical features of all subsequent versions: it uses somewhat sensational language, repeats the basic rumor (naming it as "Lights Out!"), and provides a validating reference (i.e., the bank's memo format); it also localizes the supposed criminal plans, alludes in a vague way to specific cases, and recommends a course of action.

Later versions of the warning—usually computer-written and often laser-printed—tend to have more exclamation points (sometimes coming before as well as after sentences), to have more words or whole lines printed in all caps or underlined (sometimes double-underlined, and sometimes both all caps and underlined), and often to have handwritten additions like *"This is not a joke,"* or *"Be careful out there,"* or *"Urgent!"* A few examples were hand-lettered and photocopied or were retyped on a company's letterhead (including the City of Detroit Water and Sewerage Department). Most examples that I collected had been faxed; others were e-mailed, sent by post-office mail, or posted as hard-copy memos on bulletin boards.

Dates on these warnings range from early September to early December 1993, most coming in mid-September. Other cities mentioned in them are St. Louis, Detroit, Dallas, Atlanta, Norfolk (Virginia), New York, Baltimore, Los Angeles, Sacramento, and Honolulu. (Articles in the press added Memphis, Toledo, Columbus, Pittsburgh, Philadelphia, Washington, D.C., Minneapolis, Little Rock, Tulsa, Houston, San Antonio, Lubbock, Denver, Salt Lake City, San Jose, and San Francisco, Letters from readers added cities in New Jersey, Florida, Missouri, and the Northwest. Clearly, the "Lights Out!" rumor was flying coast to coast.) The institutions circulating the fliers were banks, businesses, law firms, universities, military posts, hospitals, and day-care centers. Several of the warning notices contain routing stamps or slips indicating that they were circulated throughout a whole office or company.

About mid-September the warnings began to name "Grady Harn of the Sacramento Police Department" as the source of the information. Also, the weekend of September 25 and 26 was pinpointed as "Blood [or Bloods'] Initiation Weekend," when, supposedly, gangs, including the notorious Bloods Gang, would hold their murderous initiation.[1] A few of the fliers, although unsigned, made first-person reference to "my stepfather" or to another relative who had "called me" with this important information. Some fliers admitted that "this information has not been confirmed," but most fliers still advised readers not to flash their lights at anyone, just in case. One person sending me a printed flier added in a note: "One of our stupidvisers [at work] stood up and read this to us." After the supposed "Bloods' Weekend" came and went without incident, the fliers—now minus the dates—continued to appear, mostly in fax machines.

During the 1993 autumn semester at Indiana University at Kokomo a folklore class studied the "Lights Out!" rumor. The instructor, Susanne Ridlen, forwarded a packet of the twenty items resulting from the project, and these display the variations of the story in one community and of the means by which it was transmitted.

The Kokomo students documented transmission of "Lights Out!" via word of mouth, telephone (including long-distance calls), on both commercial and CB radio, via e-mail, fax, printed memos (distributed in schools and workplaces), and in publications. Several Kokomo versions combined "Lights Out!" with other car-related legends (Brunvand 1981: 19–46; 1984: 50–68; 1986: 49–67; 1989: 89–128), and some people claimed that the gang initiations included the cutting off of feet or ears. The specific gangs involved were said to be the Crypts [sic] and the Bloods, groups said to be moving to Kokomo either south from Chicago or north from Indianapolis. Other versions claimed an origin of the information from Mississippi, where such initiations supposedly had occurred. Motorists would be targeted either if they blinked (or "flickered") their lights or if they honked at a gang car driving without lights. Police were said to be warning motorists—via gas-station attendants—not to flash their lights. Despite this, two (or three) people, according to the Kokomo rumors, had already died.

A story in the *Kokomo Tribune* on October 14, ("Police Shoot Hole in Gang Initiation Rumor") described "Lights Out!" as a baseless rumor that was thought to have reached Kokomo from Jackson, Mississippi, on September 19 in a message broadcast on CB radio. Both Indiana and Illinois state police gang-crimes units were quoted in the news story as denying the rumor.

(Similarly, the Salt Lake City Police Department on September 24 issued a news release calling the "Lights Out!" story "unfounded . . . unsubstantiated and without merit." Many police departments across the nation issued similar denials.)

The letters (including e-mail, mail, and faxed correspondence) that I received from readers of my books commenting on the "Lights Out!" rumor add to the sketchy story a few more details that must have circulated orally, since they do not appear in the printed fliers. These letters were dated from mid-September 1993 to April 11, 1994, and came from people who knew or suspected that the story was false. Most letters reported a chain of informal communication of the story—i.e., a co-worker whose girlfriend, a nurse, had heard about someone working on the other shift at the hospital or at a different hospital who had treated victims of the ritual. The initiations, according to some writers, "were supposed to test the mental toughness" of gang recruits. Sometimes the gang recruits would trace the offending cars via their license plates. The police were not publicizing the crimes, according to rumors, in order to lull gangs into a false sense of security in hopes that they could be caught in the act. A letter dated March 29, 1994, from New Cumberland, Pennsylvania, reported a variation in the story: "Cars Full of Satan Worshippers Driving Around Without Their Headlights." The writer had overheard his secretary warning her sister about the threat, and she had heard it from the driver of her van pool, who had heard it from a friend who saw a sign warning people about it in a store window.

A Seattle reader in a letter dated September 24 (the Friday before "Bloods' Weekend") mentioned that on Thursday the twenty-third the flier appeared at her workplace and "to my distress, every one of my twelve co-workers fell for it . . . despite my insistence that it couldn't possibly be true." Meanwhile, in Salt Lake City in my own department at the university, here's what happened—or *nearly* happened—on the same days. On the twenty-third, a reader from Fort Lauderdale, Florida, faxed me a letter saying he was also faxing a copy of a memo that he suspected was based on a rumor; page 2 of the fax transmission was the "Lights Out!" warning itself, typed on the letterhead of a Florida Jewish community center. The secretary of my department pulled page 1 of the message and put it into my mailbox without reading it beyond the address. Page 2—the warning memo—however, she read with alarm and then took it with her on Friday to a full departmental meeting; or, not *quite* a full meeting, since I myself, as a partial retiree, had decided to skip town that afternoon. The secretary intended to read the notice to the assembled faculty in order to alert them not to flash their lights when driving home, but she was dissuaded from doing so by my colleague, folklorist Margaret Brady. Brady convinced her that the warning was just "one of those legends that people are always sending Jan." Our secretary still felt the story might be true, since her own daughter had also heard about it in Salt Lake City a few days earlier.

The news stories about "Lights Out!" may be taken in chronological order, insofar as dates can be determined from the clippings.

As mentioned earlier, the first clipping I have is from the *Memphis Commercial Appeal* of August 14. The second is from the *Daily Southtown*, a suburban Chicago paper, on September 11 ("Police Say Area Story of Gang Rite Is Hoax"). The lead reads: "It's a great story—just like most so-called 'urban legends.'" Besides describing the same "anonymous handbills," this news story quotes police officials who deny it and adds that it sounds like something that might happen "in the frozen wastelands of Russia." The news story also suggests the possibility of copycat crimes, and it concludes with the threat of prosecution against spreaders of the tale. Every facet of this fairly obscure little news item turns out to be typical of what most papers wrote.

Four days later, on September 15, Mary Schmich, a *Chicago Tribune* columnist, wrote about the rumor, calling it "urban faxlore." Schmich identified the Black Gangster Disciple Nation as the Chicago street gang blamed for the outrage, but she emphasized that the rumor was unsubstantiated and strongly denied by Chicago police. Schmich listed radio stations, colleges, hospitals, churches, and video stores as places where the warning had appeared. Because she had phoned me to discuss the rumor, Schmich was able to cite the earlier Memphis example of the story and also to compare "Lights Out!" to other urban lore about crime and violence. (Mary Schmich said that she was calling me at the suggestion of folklorist Alan Dundes of U.C. Berkeley, whom she had called earlier. He had not yet heard about the warnings but thought that I might have.)

At this point my phone began ringing off the hook, and I was preparing to leave on an extended trip; so I put a message on my answering machine saying, in effect, "No interviews, please." I decided to stay out of the spotlight and see what reporters might make of the rumor on their own, or with the help of other folklorists whom they might contact.

Shortly after taking this vow of silence I started to see results: on September 18 two papers ran stories—the Little Rock *Arkansas Democrat-Gazette* ("Gang Initiation Rumor Baseless, LR Police Say") and the *San Jose Mercury News* ("Cops Try to Arrest Rumor of Gang Rite"). The enterprising Arkansas reporter located three of the Brunvand books and compared "Lights Out!" to other urban lore, including an earlier local outbreak of "The Mutilated Boy" legend (Brunvand 1984: 78–92; 1986: 148–156). The even more enterprising San Jose reporter managed to get a Memphis Police spokesman and Alan Dundes on the phone. From Tennessee she learned that the story was known in Knoxville and Chattanooga as well; from Dundes (who now had heard the story and had a comment ready for it) she picked up the term *faxlore* and also the ideas that a fear of teenagers—especially gang members—was reflected in the story and that it might be inspired by acts of violence against tourists in Florida. In an unusual twist, the *Mercury News* withheld details of the warnings, fearing, they said, to suggest copycat crimes. This article also referred to the speed with which the rumor had blanketed Silicon Valley, where thousands of people are linked to e-mail and to computer bulletin boards.

In Salt Lake City (where I also dodged the press) another gang rumor was flying—that gangs were planning to rape a cheerleader as part of an initiation. Although police and school authorities denied the rumor, a September 18 article in the *Deseret News* reported widespread concern among students and parents, especially on the more affluent east side of the Salt Lake Valley. One television station was criticized for publicizing the story, even though the broadcast had made it clear that the rumors were unconfirmed.

Meanwhile, back in Chicago, on September 21, the student newspaper of the University of Illinois branch there was debunking the story again. One version of the warning photocopied on a state police letterhead was described as having a typeface that did not match the rest of the letterhead, a clue to its unreliability. On September 22, the *Houston Post,* the *Houston Chronicle,* and the *Toledo Blade* ran articles on the rumor. The *Post* article ("Scary Gang Rumor Has Its Fax All Wrong") was pretty standard, except for calling the warning "an electronic chain letter" and "an urban myth[!]" (Maybe I should have answered the phone after all.) The *Chronicle* article ("HPD Tries to Stop Rumor About Gang Rites") had a novel touch—a color photograph of a grinning police chief holding up one of the fliers; the "Dragnet"-inspired caption read, "Just a phony fax, ma'am." The chief was quoted as saying, "I'd rather deal with the gangs than talk to any more hysterical people on the phone."

A sidelight of the Texas circulation of the rumor was revealed September 23 in a column in the *San Antonio Express-News.* Columnist Roddy Stinson, who a week earlier had dubbed his own city "the wide-eyed booby capital of the nation" for panicking over the "Lights Out!" urban legend (Stinson's term), now gave the booby prize to Houston, where the story had circulated earlier.

During "Bloods' Weekend" itself—September 25 and 26—the newspaper stories increased: I have clippings from papers in central New Jersey, San Francisco, Los Angeles, Salt Lake City, Minneapolis, and Pittsburgh. The New Jersey story mentions dozens of calls to police from fearful people, spurred by warnings traced to the Johnson & Johnson headquarters in New Brunswick and also circulated in area colleges and high schools and in a large insurance company. The San Francisco article ("Rumors Fly on Computer Networks") also names hospitals as hotbeds of the story, but emphasizes computer rather than faxed transmission. Alan Dundes is quoted anew, this time with a different slant on the story. "There is an element of the car, which represents power, mobility, and sex," the Berkeley professor comments, adding that the rumor was probably fueled by recent shootings of foreign tourists in Florida.

The *L.A. Times* article of September 24 is the first publication to mention the mysterious Grady Harn of the Sacramento Police Department, who is named on many fliers; the *Times* checked with Sacramento and found that no one of that name serves on the police force there. Another innovation in the *Times* story is an unattributed claim that "the warnings are the work of a computer hacker who used facsimile telephone numbers to disseminate the messages." The fliers are described as "clumsily worded," which suggests, perhaps, poor social or communicative skills of the assumed hacker. Finally, the *L.A. Times* mentions that these phony warnings are "the latest examples of what sociologists call an urban myth." Although Los Angeles gang investigators are quoted in the story, the reporters who wrote the piece did not attempt to interview any gang members themselves.

Both Salt Lake City newspapers now covered the story, each relating it to the earlier rumors about gang intentions to rape cheerleaders. One county sheriff in

Utah said he had not been able to get off the phone for more than 30 seconds at a time while fielding calls about "Lights Out!" from citizens and from the press. In a technically garbled explanation of how the story may have started, a police official suggested that "the hoax note was faxed into a billboard computer system."

Probably "Bloods' Weekend" was when the Associated Press circulated an article debunking "Lights Out!" that was widely reprinted and quoted. (I do not have a dated copy of the AP release.) The AP story quoted Ralph Rosnow and Gary Fine, coauthors of a book on rumor and gossip. Fine voiced the opinion that "*gang* in this particular rumor is a code word for poor, young black men."

The Minneapolis news article of September 25 again described the suspected villain in the case as a "hacker," but the paper associated "hacking" with *faxing* messages rather than with using computerized e-mail or a computer bulletin board. Articles published in Pittsburgh on September 25 and 27 added little to the picture except for speculating that the rumor came from "an unidentified originator in California."

In an interesting juxtaposition, the *Baltimore Sun* on September 27 ran a long story debunking the "Blue Star Acid" rumor (Brunvand 1984:162–169; 1989: 55–64), which had cropped up there again recently with a sidebar story on "Lights Out!" The Baltimore version was that members of "the Los Angeles-based gang the Bloods were randomly shooting motorists as part of a nationwide initiation campaign."

At last the rumor was mentioned in the national press. In the September 27 issue of *U.S. News & World Report,* a column by John Leo mentioned "Lights Out!" in passing as "a new bit of urban folklore." The column was mostly devoted to comments on the shootings of foreign tourists in Florida. *Newsweek,* in a brief notice headlined "Big Fax Attack," mentioned Houston, Los Angeles, and Atlanta as sites of the rumor. In a syndicated column of September 29, William Raspberry of the *Washington Post* mentioned the rumor, although he indicated that just "people" (gangs were not mentioned) were driving with their lights off, hoping to entice victims to flash their headlights at them and thus become targets for violence.

The last weekend of September the magazine section of the *Dallas Observer* ran a detailed account titled "Anatomy of a Rumor: How the Gang-Initiation Story Terrified Dallas." The author called it "something of a minor urban myth in several cities," and he did a creditable job of tracking local versions back to individuals who had picked it up while traveling, on the phone, via fax, and so on. According to the *Observer,* one Dallas businessman said he was handed the warning "when he boarded an American Airlines return flight from Tampa."

From October to mid-December only a few further news stories appeared; the cities that were late to catch the rumor were Denver; Philadelphia and Allentown, Pennsylvania; Columbus, Ohio; and Lubbock, Texas. With Lubbock, on

December 14, my clipping file bottoms out. The Denver story was mainly about rumors of gang rapes at a mall, with "Lights Out!" mentioned only in passing. The *Philadelphia Inquirer* story was unrestrained in calling the rumor "a big, fat, stinking, Pinocchio-nose kind of lie," but added, "and everybody believes it." Ralph Rosnow, who teaches at Temple University, was again quoted. The *Allentown Morning Call* story mentioned that the rumor had been retyped on Thomas Jefferson University security letterhead; both Patricia Turner, a professor at U.C. Davis, and Alan Dundes were quoted in this story, evidently from original interviews by the Allentown writer. Turner made some interesting observations about the theme of the "demonized outsider" threatening a Good Samaritan on the road. Dundes repeated some of his earlier remarks, and he too touched on the "Good Samaritan" theme.

In Columbus, "Lights Out!" got only a short paragraph in a story that was primarily about another rumor—that groups are trying to raise funds to buy firearms for the homeless. Similarly, in Lubbock, Texas, "Lights Out!" rated only a short mention in a full-page feature story about "Those pesky rumors." The only unusual touch here was the remark of a local police sergeant about how he deals with the panicky public in such cases; he said, "I just try to sound authoritative and reassuring." By mid-December, then, the story was effectively dead in the nation's media, although a few individuals continued to write me letters about it.

Unexpectedly, "Lights Out!" emerged one more time in the national media in "Traps," a new CBS-TV police drama, in which George C. Scott plays Joe Trapcheck, a former homicide investigator who comes out of retirement to serve as a consultant in his old department. In the premiere episode, aired on Thursday, March 31, 1994, he has joined the "Headlight Killer Taskforce," which is working to solve a series of shootings that occurred after people gave a "courtesy blink" to a car driving with its headlights out. Curiously, the episode also included another piece of urban folklore, where a photocopy machine is used to fool a suspect into revealing needed information; he is told that he's actually hooked up to a new type of polygraph (Brunvand 1993:139–145).

Reviewing the "Lights Out!" phenomenon, briefly, as *folklore*, it seems evident that although modern technology and communications facilitated the rapid dissemination of the rumor over an extremely broad area, the variations that developed were similar to those typically caused by oral transmission alone. Details were added and altered; the story was localized; authorities were invoked to support the story; supposed actual cases were cited, and so on. "Lights Out!" was similar to other recent rumors and legends, including "Blue Star Acid" (also fax- and photocopy-delivered), "The Assailant in the Backseat" and other car horror stories, "The Attempted Abduction" and other mall-crime stories, and the like. *Faxlore* is a catchy term, but it is not clear that it should imply any essentially different kind of modern tradition.

Despite the sensational tone of the warnings, their informal channels of distribution, their poor English usage, and their lack of any specific verification, their message was taken to heart by many Americans. Thousands of people must have duplicated and distributed the fliers for them to have penetrated so widely. I believe the folklorists and sociologists who commented on "Lights Out!" were right in identifying themes like teenage and gang crimes, racism, urban problems, and attacks on foreign motorists as topics underlying the "Lights Out!" hysteria. (I'm not sure, however, where the sex, mentioned by Alan Dundes, comes in.) A well-known gang name, the Bloods, lent itself perfectly to intensifying the hysteria, as did another name, the Cryps (when misunderstood as "Crypts"). In Chicago, a gang with the very word "Black" in its name—the Black Gangster Disciple Nation—fed into this same racial fear, and in Kokomo the idea that the warning had come from Mississippi implies the same stereotype.

Press reports reveal other views of the rumor flap. Journalists tended to confuse terms like *myth, rumor, legend, chain letter,* and *hoax,* as well as to ignore the technical differences between fax, E-mail, and computer bulletin boards or computer newsgroups. Several newspapers mentioned copycat crimes, although none of the papers ever reported any actual "Lights Out!" crimes *or* copycats. In hope of determining the precise origin of the rumor—something folklorists seldom seek or find—journalists focused upon (indeed, may have *invented*) the *hoaxing hacker* character, presumably someone from California. No evidence for the existence of such a hoaxer was ever presented. An idea proposed by both law-enforcement and newspaper sources is that the originator of the story should be found and prosecuted. Despite having this serious plan in mind, newspapers felt free to pun shamelessly in the wording of their stories and headlines: "just the fax," "a fax attack," "has its fax all wrong," "guns down the rumor," and others.

One persistent fear that both the general public and newspapers responded to was the idea of dangerous gang activity entering one's own community from some outside source, usually a nearby larger city that is thought to be awash with gang crimes. It still amazes me (as mentioned above) that no investigative reporter seems to have bothered to have contacted any local gang members to ask about initiation rituals in general and about "Lights Out!" or other car-related customs in particular.

Finally, I re-emphasize one theme of the warnings pointed out in only a single news article among the reports I collected. This is the "Good Samaritan" theme mentioned by Turner and Dundes. Flashing one's headlights at a car driving toward you at night without its lights on is a simple, common act of courtesy and safety. It's something most drivers have been taught to do, either by a driver's education teacher or simply by customary example from other drivers. (I'll be so bold as to call this a folk custom.) Some of the warning fliers allude to this custom by referring to it as a "courtesy flash." (I'll concede, however, that light flashing may also imply negative criticism in the minds of some drivers who flash or are flashed at.) Another strong message of "Lights Out!" then, is that something you, as a driver, have learned to do as a good and socially useful thing may, in this crime-ridden modern world, have become an act of aggression toward another driver who represents an outsider to your standards of behavior—perhaps a younger person of a different race who belongs to a street gang—and this outsider will go so far as to murder you for daring to be courteous. In other words, the "Lights Out!" rumor says, "Forget about being a courteous driver, because *it might kill you!*"

Note

1. Folklorist Ed Kahn of Berkeley, California, pointed out to me the similarity to the much-feared "Michelangelo" computer virus, supposedly set to strike DOS-based machines worldwide on March 6 (the Renaissance master's birthdate), 1992. Like the "DataCrime" (or "Friday the 13th") virus of 1989, this threat proved to be much less destructive than predicted.

References

Brunvand, Jan Harold. 1981. *The Vanishing Hitchhiker: American Urban Legends and Their Meanings.* New York: W.W. Norton.

———. 1984. *The Choking Doberman and Other "New" Urban Legends.* New York: W. W. Norton .

———.1986. *The Mexican Pet: More "New" Urban Legends and Some Old Favorites.* New York: W.W. Norton.

———. 1989. *Curses! Broiled Again! The Hottest Urban Legends Going.* New York: W. W. Norton.

———. 1993. *The Baby Train and Other Lusty Urban Legends.* New York: W. W. Norton.

The Ten-Percent Myth

by BENJAMIN RADFORD

Someone has taken most of your brain away and you probably didn't even know it. Well, not taken your brain away, exactly, but decided that you don't use it. It's the old myth heard time and again about how people use only ten percent of their brains. While for the people who repeat that myth, it's probably true, the rest of us happily use all of our brains.

The Myth and the Media

That tired Ten-Percent claim pops up all the time. In 1998, a national magazine ads for U.S. Satellite Broadcasting showed a drawing of a brain. Under it was the caption, "You only use 11 percent of its potential." Well, they're a little closer than the ten-percent figure, but still off by about 89 percent. In July 1998, ABC television ran promotional spots for *The Secret Lives of Men*, one of their offerings for the fall season's lineup. The spot featured a full-screen blurb that read, "Men only use ten percent of their brains."

One reason this myth has endured is that it has been adopted by psychics and other paranormal pushers to explain psychic powers. On more than one occasion I've heard psychics tell their audiences, "We only use ten percent of our minds. If scientists don't know what we do with the other ninety percent, it must be used for psychic powers!" In *Reason To Believe: A Practical Guide to Psychic Phenomena*, author Michael Clark mentions a man named Craig Karges. Karges charges a lot of money for his "Intuitive Edge" program, designed to develop natural psychic abilities. Clark quotes Karges as saying: "We normally use only 10 to 20 percent of our minds. Think how different your life would be if you could utilize that other 80 to 90 percent known as the subconscious mind" (Clark 1997, 56).

This was also the reason that Caroline Myss gave for her alleged intuitive powers on a segment of *Eye to Eye with Bryant Gumbel*, which aired in

July of 1998. Myss, who has written books on unleashing "intuitive powers," said that everyone has intuitive gifts, and lamented that we use so little of the mind's potential. To make matters worse, just the week before, on the very same program, correct information was presented about the myth. In a bumper spot between the program and commercials, a quick quiz flashed onscreen: What percentage of the brain is used? The multiple-choice answers ranged from 10 percent to 100 percent. The correct answer appeared, which I was glad to see. But if the producers knew that what one of their interviewees said is clearly and demonstrably inaccurate, why did they let it air? Does the right brain not know what the left brain is doing? Perhaps the Myss interview was a repeat, in which case the producers presumably checked her facts after it aired and felt some responsibility to correct the error in the following week's broadcast. Or possibly the broadcasts aired in sequence and the producers simply did not care and broadcast Myss and her misinformation anyway.

Even Uri Geller, who has made a career out of trying to convince people he can bend metal with his mind, trots out this little gem. This claim appears in his book *Uri Geller's Mind-Power Book* in the introduction: "Our minds are capable of remarkable, incredible feats, yet we don't use them to their full capacity. In fact, *most of us only use about 10 per cent of our brains,* if that. The other 90 per cent is full of untapped potential and undiscovered abilities, which means our minds are only operating in a very limited way instead of at full stretch. I believe that *we once had full power over our minds.* We had to, in order to survive, but as our world has become more sophisticated and complex we have forgotten many of the abilities we once had" (emphasis in original).

Evidence Against the Ten-Percent Myth

The argument that psychic powers come from the unused majority of the brain is based on the logical fallacy of the argument from ignorance. In this fallacy, lack of proof for a position (or simply lack of information) is used to try to support a particular claim. Even if it were true that the vast majority of the human mind is unused (which it clearly is not), that fact in no way implies that any extra capacity could somehow give people paranormal powers. This fallacy pops up all the time in paranormal claims, and is especially prevalent among UFO proponents. For example: Two people see a strange light in the sky. The first, a UFO believer, says, "See there! Can you explain that?" The skeptic replies that no, he can't. The UFO believer is gleeful. "Ha! You don't know what it is, so it must be aliens!" he says, arguing from ignorance.

What follows are two of the reasons that the Ten-Percent story is suspect. (For a much more thorough and detailed analysis of the subject, see Barry

Beyerstein's chapter in *Mind Myths: Exploring Everyday Mysteries of the Mind* [2000].)

1) Brain imaging research techniques such as PET scans (positron emission tomography) and fMRI (functional magnetic resonance imaging) clearly show that the vast majority of the brain does not lie fallow. Indeed, although certain minor functions may use only a small part of the brain at one time, any sufficiently complex set of activities or thought patterns will indeed use many parts of the brain. Just as people don't use all of their muscle groups at one time, they also don't use all of their brain at once. For any given activity, such as eating, watching television, making love, or reading *Bizarre Cases*, you may use a few specific parts of your brain. Over the course of a whole day, however, just about all of the brain is used at one time or another.

2) The myth presupposes an extreme localization of functions in the brain. If the "used" or "necessary" parts of the brain were scattered all around the organ, that would imply that much of the brain is in fact necessary. But the myth implies that the "used" part of the brain is a discrete area, and the "unused" part is like an appendix or tonsil, taking up space but essentially unnecessary. But if all those parts of the brain are unused, removal or damage to the "unused" part of the brain should be minor or unnoticed. Yet people who have suffered head trauma, a stroke, or other brain injury are frequently severely impaired. Have you ever heard a doctor say, ". . . But luckily when that bullet entered his skull, it only damaged the 90 percent of his brain he didn't use"? Of course not.

Variants of the Ten-Percent Myth

The myth is not simply a static, misunderstood factoid. It has several forms, and this adaptability gives it a shelf life longer than lacquered Spam. In the basic form, the myth claims that years ago a scientist discovered that we indeed did use only ten percent of our brains. Another variant is that only ten percent of the brain had been *mapped,* and this in turn became misunderstood as ten percent *used.* A third variant was described earlier by Craig Karges. This view is that the brain is somehow divided neatly into two parts: the conscious mind which is used ten to twenty percent of the time (presumably at capacity); and the subconscious mind, where the remaining eighty to ninety percent of the brain is unused. This description betrays a profound misunderstanding of brain function research.

Part of the reason for the long life of the myth is that if one variant can be proven incorrect, the person who held the belief can simply shift the reason for his belief to another basis, while the belief itself stays intact. So, for example, if a person is shown that PET scans depict activity throughout the entire brain, he can still claim that, well, the ninety percent figure really referred to the *subconscious* mind, and therefore the Ten-Percent figure is still basically correct.

Regardless of the exact version heard, the myth is spread and repeated, by both the well-meaning and the deliberately deceptive. The belief that remains, then, is what Robert J. Samuelson termed a "psycho-fact, [a] belief that, though not supported by hard evidence, is taken as real because its constant repetition changes the way we experience life." People who don't know any better will repeat it over and over, until, like the admonition against swimming right after you eat, the claim is widely believed. ("Triumph of the Psycho-Fact," *Newsweek,* May 9, 1994.)

The origins of the myth are not at all clear. Beyerstein, of the Brain Behaviour Laboratory at Simon Fraser University in British Columbia, has traced it back to at least the early part of the century. A column in *New Scientist* magazine also suggested various roots, including Albert Einstein and Dale Carnegie (Brain Drain 1999). It likely has a number of sources, principally misunderstood or misinterpreted legitimate scientific findings as well as self-help gurus.

The most powerful lure of the myth is probably the idea that we might develop psychic abilities, or at least gain a leg up on the competition by improving our memory or concentration. All this is available for the asking, the ads say, if we just tapped into our most incredible of organs, the brain.

It is past time to put this myth to rest, although if it has survived at least a century so far, it will surely live on into the next millennium. Perhaps the best way to combat this chestnut is to reply to the speaker, when the myth is mentioned, "Oh? What part don't you use?"

Acknowledgment

I am indebted to Dr. Barry Beyerstein for providing research help and suggestions.

References

Beyerstein, Barry. 2000. Whence cometh the myth that we only use ten percent of our brains? In *Mind-myths: Exploring Everyday Mysteries of the Mind and Brain,* edited by Sergio Della Sala. New York: John Wiley and Sons.

Brain Drain. 1999. The Last Word (column). *New Scientist* 19/26 December 1998–2 January 1999.

Clark, Michael. 1997. *Reason to Believe.* New York: Avon Books

Geller, Uri, and Jane Struthers. 1996. *Uri Geller's Mind-power Book.* London: Virgin Books.

MIND GAMES

Hidden Messages and the Bible Code

by DAVID E. THOMAS

Bible Code: The Book

A book entitled *The Bible Code* came out in June 1997 and occupied the best-seller lists for months. It is written by journalist Michael Drosnin, who claims that the Hebrew Bible contains a very complex code that reveals events that took place thousands of years after the Bible was written. Drosnin contends that some foretold events later happened exactly as predicted.

The book has been reviewed widely and has prompted articles in *Newsweek* and *Time*. Drosnin has also been making the rounds of the talk-show circuit, including the *Oprah Winfrey Show* in June 1997. *Time* said that Warner has reportedly bought the movie rights (Van Biema 1997).

Drosnin's technique is heavily based on that of Eliyahu Rips of Hebrew University in Israel, who published an article entitled "Equidistant Letter Sequences in the Book of Genesis" in the journal *Statistical Science* (Witztum, Rips, and Rosenburg 1994). Like Rips, Drosnin arranges the 304,805 Hebrew letters of the Bible into a large array. Spaces and punctuation marks are omitted, and words are run together one after another. A computer looks for matches to selected names or words by stepping to every nth letter in the array. One can go forward or backward; and for each value of "step distance," n, there are n different starting letters. Drosnin's match for "Yitzhak Rabin" had a step value n equal to 4,772.

Both Rips and Drosnin work with the original Hebrew characters, which are said to have been given by God to Moses one character at a time, with no spaces or punctuation, just as they appear in "the code." The code is considered to exist only in the Hebrew Bible and not in translations or any other books. The code concept, however, can be easily demonstrated with English characters. Consider the following verse from the King James Version (KJV) of the Book of Genesis:

31:28 And hast not suffered me to kiss my sons and my daughters? thou hast now done foolishly in so doing.

If you start at the R in "daughters," and skip over three letters to the O in "thou," and three more to the S in "hast," and so on, the hidden message "Roswell" is revealed! This message has a step value of 4, as shown in figure 1.

G H T E⟦R⟧S T H⟦O⟧U H A⟦S⟧T N O⟦W⟧D O N⟦E⟧F O O⟦L⟧I S H⟦L⟧Y I N S

Figure 1. "Roswell" hidden in KJV Genesis 31:28.

When Drosnin finds a name or word match for a given step value n, he then rearranges the letters into a huge matrix (which he calls a "crossword puzzle"). The matrix is n letters wide, and inside this puzzle, the letters for the "hidden message" line up together vertically. (Sometimes, a slightly different procedure is used to make the hidden word run diagonally, every other row, and so forth.) The analyst or the computer can then look for more keyword-related "hits" around the given hidden word. Secondary matches can be picked off vertically, horizontally, or diagonally. Drosnin found the word "Dallas" (connected with keywords "President Kennedy") in one of his puzzles by starting at a D, and then picking the next letters by moving one space over to the right and three spaces down several times.

An example of such a matrix for the "Roswell" mention in KJV Genesis appears in figure 2. The letters of "Roswell" now appear vertically at the center of the puzzle. The actual matrix of unique letters is only four characters wide here (dashed box), but I took the liberty of showing extra letters for context. A companion hidden message—"UFO"—is indicated within circle symbols. This "UFO" is itself a hidden message with a step value of 12. Drosnin accepts any such messages, even words running *horizontally* (i.e., the actual words of the Bible strung together). If either "Roswell" or "UFO" had been found encoded in the Hebrew Bible, Drosnin would not have hesitated to use words from the direct text as a "match" (for example, the words "thou hast now done foolishly.")

S A N D M Y D A U G H T E R S T H O U H
M Y D A U G H T E R S T H O U H A S T N
U G H T E R S T H O U H A S T N O W D O
E R S T H O U H A S T N O W D O N E F O
H O U H A S T N O W D O N E F O O L I S
A S T N O W D O N E F O O L I S H L Y I
O W D O N E F O O L I S H L Y I N S O D
N E F O O L I S H L Y I N S O D O I N G
O L I S H L Y I N S O D O I N G I T I S
H L Y I N S O D O I N G I T I S I N T H

Figure 2. Matrix or "crossword puzzle" for "Roswell/UFO" hidden in KJV Genesis.

The unusual pairing of "Roswell" and "UFO" is shown in linear form in figure 3. This match is as stunning as any described in Drosnin's book—yet none claim that the Bible code would have translated gracefully over to the KJV Genesis.

T E ⓇR S T H ⓄⓄ H A ⓈT N O ⓌD O N E Ⓕ O O Ⓛ I S H Ⓛ Y I N S Ⓞ D O

Figure 3. "Roswell" and "UFO" hidden in KJV Genesis 31:28.

Drosnin claims mathematical proof that "no human could have encoded the Bible in this way" (Drosnin 1997, 50–51). He says, "I do not know if it is God," but adds that the code proves "we are not alone."

Hidden Messages

Some believe that these "messages" in the Hebrew Bible are not just coincidence—they were put there deliberately by God. But if someone finds a hidden message in a book, a song played backwards, funny-looking Martian mesas, or some other object or thing, does that prove someone *else* put the message there *intentionally?* Or might the message exist only in the eyes of the beholder (and in those of his or her followers)? Does perception of meaning prove the message was deliberately created?

Most of the data cited in favor of the purported intelligent alien construction of the "Face on Mars" is based on mathematical relationships among various Martian structures and locations. For example, author Richard Hoagland finds the "Cydonian" ratio (the "face" lies on the Cydonia plains region of Mars), e/π, in the tangent of the face's latitude of 40.868 degrees north, in the ratios of angles of the D&M Pyramid, and in numerous other places (Hoagland 1992). Does that mean the "face" and "city" on Mars were "designed" for the express purpose of spreading that very message? Hoagland emphatically says, "Yes!" My inner skeptic says, "Not so fast!"

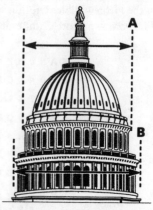

In my research into such phenomena, I have found numerous instances of Hoagland's Martian ratios on objects we know were not designed or built by aliens, such as the U.S. Capitol rotunda (figure 4). Does that prove that Martians built this structure? Or is this phenomenon related mainly to the determination and skill of the person looking for a spe-

Figure 4. The "Martian" ratio $e/\pi \cong$ A/B, hidden in the Capitol rotunda (precise measurements of A and B yield A/B $\cong$ 0.863, while $e/\pi \cong$ 2.71828/3.14159 $\cong$ 0.865, an error of less than one half of one percent).

cial message? *Any* special message?

There are dozens of books about Nostradamus. In one (Hewitt and Lorie 1991), the authors find hidden predictions by scrambling the seer's quatrains (in French, no less), and then decoding according to an extremely complicated and mysterious formula. The back cover prominently displays one such unscrambled prediction: "1992—George Bush re-elected." (Wrong.) The authors should have known that it's much safer to find hidden predictions of events that have already happened.

Some critics of Drosnin say the journalist is just "data mining." Mathematician Brendan McKay of Australian National University and his colleagues searched Hebrew texts besides the Bible. They found fifty-nine words related to Chanukah in the Hebrew translation of *War and Peace*. But McKay doesn't think someone engineered this remarkable feat for his or anyone's benefit. Since then, McKay has responded to the following challenge Drosnin made in *Newsweek*: "When my critics find a message about the assassination of a prime minister encrypted in *Moby Dick*, I'll believe them" (Begley 1997). McKay found assassination "predictions" in *Moby Dick* for Indira Gandhi, Rene Moawad, Leon Trotsky, Rev. M. L. King, and Robert F. Kennedy (see http://cs.anu.edu. au/~bdm/dilugim/moby.html). Eliyahu Rips himself has denied Drosnin's implication that they worked together, and has said, "I do not support the book as it is or the conclusions it derives" (Van Biema 1997).

Hidden Names in KJV Genesis and *Edwards v. Aguillard*

I have very recently carried out a study on finding hidden names in both the KJV Genesis and the U.S. Supreme Court's 1987 ruling on *Edwards v. Aguillard* (a well-known ruling on creationism, hereafter referred to as simply *Edwards*). I used the same set of rules for both the KJV Genesis (about 150,000 characters) and *Edwards* (about 100,000 characters). I loaded a list of preselected names and let the computer search for each one in turn, for equidistant letter sequences with step distances from 2 to 1,000, and for every possible starting letter. I searched forward only.

One would expect that special biblical messages hidden in the Hebrew Bible would simply not make it into the King James Version, much less into *Edwards*. And since the Hebrew alphabet doesn't include vowels, it should be much harder to find matches in the English texts, because an additional character match is required for each vowel.

Drosnin's control was the Hebrew text of *War and Peace*. Drosnin claims that when they searched for words (such as "comet," "Jupiter," etc.) in the Bible, they often found them there, but *not* in *War and Peace*.

I picked a set of names carefully. The list contained five names of four letters, five of five letters, five of six letters, five of seven letters, and five of either eight or nine letters. I was more whimsical in my choice of subjects and chose talk show hosts, scientists, and just plain folks as well as political or historical figures. I found *thousands* of hidden occurrences of these names in both Genesis and *Edwards*. The results appear in table 1.

It is striking that tens of thousands of hidden occurrences were found for the

Length	Name	Genesis	Edwards
4 Letters	Deer	7440	3255
	Dole	2692	1349
	Leno	3353	2836
	Newt	2554	1026
	Reed	7340	3326
5 Letters	Gould	5	4
	Oprah	49	31
	Regis	51	71
	Rosie	202	341
	Sagan	107	62
6 Letters	Asimov	1	0
	Darwin	3	1
	Hitler	18	13
	Romero	6	1
	Stalin	15	10
7 Letters	Clinton	0	0
	Frazier	0	0
	Gardner	0	1
	Hillary	0	0
	Kennedy	0	0
8 or 9 Letters	Einstein	0	0
	Gingrich	0	0
	Churchill	0	0
	Letterman	0	0
	Matsumura	0	0
	Sum	23836	12327

Table 1. Counts of hidden words found in KJV Genesis and *Edwards* v. *Aguillard*, at steps of 1,000 or less, forward only.

twenty-five names submitted, for both Genesis and *Edwards*. More matches were found in the former, but it does have 50,000 more letters to work with. Another important observation is immediately apparent in table 1—short names like "Leno" or "Reed" were found much more frequently than long names like "Gingrich" or "Matsumura." ("Matsumura" is, of course, Molleen Matsumura of the National Center for Science Education, in Berkeley, and "Romero" is Albuquerque boxer Danny Romero.) "Martin Gardner" was found hidden in *Edwards,* much as Gardner anticipated could happen in his discussion of gematria and the work of Rips and his colleagues (Gardner 1997).

The results are clear and compelling, and certainly not surprising. It is much easier to find short names than long names. There might be thousands of occurrences of the four-letter name "Rich," for example. But matching "Gingrich" is much harder, since few or none of the thousands of instances of "Rich" will be preceded by "Ging" at exactly the right step locations. But there are 2,554 hidden occurrences of "Newt" in KJV Genesis, so one could *imagine* that the Speaker of the House is certainly mentioned copiously.

There is, of course, another factor in the success of hidden word searches. Simply put, some letters are more common than others. Figures 5a and 5b give the relative frequencies for the letters in Genesis and *Edwards.*

The charts show that certain letters (such as A, D, E, H, I, N, O, R, S, and T) appear more often than others. Obviously, words made with these "hot" letters (such as "Reed," "Deer," "Stalin," or "Hitler") have a better chance of being found than words containing any "cool" letters like J or Q. "Rosie" had 202 Genesis matches, more than the 49 for "Oprah"—but "Oprah" contains a cool P. (I also searched for "Harpo," which is just "Oprah" backwards, and found 62 hits.)

When I performed a separate search for "Roswell" in KJV Genesis, I only found one hidden match for this seven-letter word. But I found 5,812 matches for "UFO," 187 for "disk," five for "MOGUL," 4,798 for "NYU," two for "weather," 1,552 for "gear," seventy-seven for "crash," four for "dummy," 295 for "alien," and two for "saucer." I couldn't find "Roswell" in *Edwards* at steps of 1,000 or less, but I did find most of the others, and in similar numbers.

How Unusual Are Paired Messages?

Drosnin and others sometimes admit that finding isolated hidden names or messages can be the product of random chance. But they claim that finding *linked* pairs or triples of names or words is so improbable that doing so proves the supernatural, divine, or alien origin of the "message." In Drosnin's words,

> Consistently, the Bible code brings together interlocking words that reveal related information. With Bill Clinton, President. With the Moon landing, spaceship and Apollo 11. With Hitler, Nazi. With Kennedy, Dallas.
> In experiment after experiment, the crossword puzzles were found only in the

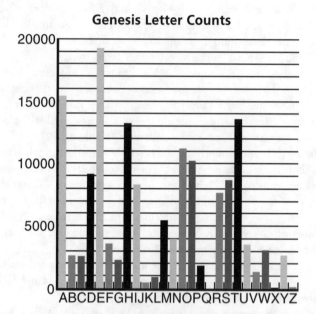

Figure 5a. Frequencies of letters of the alphabet in KJV Genesis.

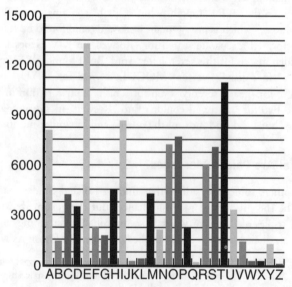

Figure 5b. Frequencies of letters of the alphabet in *Edwards* v. *Aguillard*.

Bible. Not in *War and Peace*, not in any other book, and not in ten million com-
puter-generated test cases. (Drosnin 1997, 26)

Perhaps there was a bug in Drosnin's computer program. Or perhaps he didn't
really want to find hidden message pairs outside of the Hebrew Bible. All I know
is that I was able to easily produce complex hidden messages in all the texts I
worked with.

I developed a computer program that takes various words already located as
hidden codes (such as "Hitler" and "Nazi") and plays them against each other
to find the best-linked pairs. The starting letters and equidistant steps provide
all the necessary information, provided one learns how to manipulate it.

```
COMEAFLOODTODESTROYALLFLESHANDTHEBOWSHALLBEINTHECLOUDANDIW
NANHEWASUNCOVEREDWITHINHISTENTANDHAMTHEFATHEROFCANAANSAWT
INTHETENTSOFSHEMANDCANAANSHALLBEHISSERVANTANDNOAHLIVEDAFTE
INTHEIRNATIONSANDTHESONSOFHAMCUSHANDMIZRAIMANDPHUTANDCANAA
UDIMANDANAMIMANDLEHABIMANDNAPHTUHIMANDPATHRUSIMANDCASLUHIM
IESANDINTHEIRNATIONSUNTOSHEMALSOTHEFATHEROFALLTHECHILDRENO
ONSOFJOKTANANDTHEIRDWELLINGWASFROMMESHAASTHOUGOESTUNTOSEPH
FORSTONEANDSLIMEHADTHEYFORMORTERANDTHEYSAIDGOTOLETUSBUILDU
UPONTHEFACEOFALLTHEEARTHANDTHEYLEFTOFFTOBUILDTHECITYTHEREF
LIVEDTHIRTYYEARSANDBEGATEBERANDSALAHLIVEDAFTERHEBEGATEBERF
DAFTERHEBEGATNAHORTWOHUNDREDYEARSANDBEGATSONSANDDAUGHTERSA
```

Figure 6a. Step matrix for Genesis, "Hitler/Nazi," step = 500.

```
UISIANADEPARTMENTOFEDUCATIONTHESCHOOLSUPERINTENDENTSIN
EDINTHESTATUTEABOUTPERCENTOFLOUISIANASSUPERINTENDENTSS
INTENDENTSINTERPRETEDCREATIONSCIENCEASDEFINEDBYTHEACTT
CHINGTHEVIEWTHATTHEUNIVERSEWASMADEBYACREATORIDATETHECO
GTHEINTENTOFTHELEGISLATURECONTEMPORANEOUSTOTHEPASSAGEO
THATFOUNDSTATESTATUTESTOBEUNCONSTITUTIONALHAVEBEENDISP
ONNORJOINSCONCURRINGIWRITESEPARATELYTONOTECERTAINASPEC
RETIONACCORDEDSTATEANDLOCALSCHOOLOFFICIALSINTHESELECTI
ERMINEWHETHERAPARTICULARSTATEACTIONVIOLATESTHEESTABLIS
INVOLVINGTHESENSITIVERELATIONSHIPBETWEENGOVERNMENTANDR
ARLEGISLATIVEPURPOSELEMONVKURTZMANSUPRAATSEECOMMITTEEF
THEESTABLISHMENTCLAUSEIATHESTARTINGPOINTINEVERYCASEINV
NCEDTREATMENTFORCREATIONSCIENCEANDEVOLUTIONSCIENCEACTA
TREATMENTTOCREATIONSCIENCEANDTOEVOLUTIONSCIENCEBALANCE
```

Figure 6b. Step matrix for *Edwards v. Aguillard*, "Hitler/Nazi," step = 157.

I then used this approach to develop the puzzles shown in figures 6a (Genesis, step = 500) and 6b (*Edwards,* step = 157), both with direct coded linkages of "Hitler" and "Nazi." These puzzles are striking counterexamples of Drosnin's claims.

In response to Drosnin's challenge, I decided to look for "Hitler" and "Nazi" linked in Tolstoy's *War and Peace* as well. I found an English translation of the epic novel on the Internet, and downloaded the first twenty-four chapters of Book 1, giving me about 167,000 characters. By the time I got to steps of just 750, I already had found more than half a dozen excellent puzzle linkages of "Hitler" and "Nazi." The best appears in figure 7: this entire puzzle text spans just five paragraphs of Chapter 2 of Book 1 of Tolstoy's novel.

Drosnin uses many methods to improve the odds of "impossible-by-chance" linkages. For one, he uses horizontal words taken directly from the original text. For example, when Drosnin found "Clinton" linked to "president," the word "president" was just the Hebrew word for "chief," taken from its actual context in the original Bible. Secondly, Drosnin found some hidden dates referring to the Hebrew calendar; for example, Gulf War activity on January 18, 1991, was found in the words "3rd Shevat." But, he found other dates referring to the Gregorian calendar, such as that of the Oklahoma City bombing, which was linked in the Bible by the hidden date "Day 19," and interpreted as a reference to both April 19, 1995, the date of the bombing, and April 19, 1993 (Waco). And finally, Drosnin takes full advantage of the eccentricities of the Hebrew language, in which words can be condensed and letters occasionally dropped.

My study generated several other examples that are just as spectacular, and just as unlikely (if not more so), than most of Drosnin's matches. Now, Drosnin and his colleagues would probably say that the "Roswell/UFO" connection in KJV Genesis was just a lucky break and couldn't happen again. But I found 5,812 hidden "UFO's" in Genesis, and dozens of these happen to be flying right around and *through* the hidden word "Roswell." As the puzzle step is changed, linked matches appear and disappear with astonishing frequency. Three such examples appear in figure 8, for steps of 88, 589, and 753. Hoagland claims multiple discoveries of the same hidden message are indicative of "redundancy" used by the code-maker to assure us the message is real (Hoagland 1992). But all that is really happening here is that codes can be engineered—*made* to happen. You just have to know how to harvest the field of possibilities.

Figure 9 is another striking linkage I found in KJV Genesis, 42:18 through 45:21. Here, the name "Regis" appears at a step distance of 808, but also at a step of 810, which makes a nice "X" pattern if the puzzle step is 809. (Perhaps someone should notify Regis Philbin and agents Mulder and Scully.)

If you work at any given puzzle for a while, large numbers of unexpected names and words invariably turn up. Consider the puzzle of figure 10. This text is a *contiguous* rendition of Genesis 41:38–46. This particular puzzle is easy for the reader

```
W I T H Q U I C K S H O R T S W A Y I N G S T E P S H E
E S S S A T D O W N O N A S O F A N E A R T H E S I L V
H E R S E L F A N D T O A L L A R O U N D H E R I H A V
R B A G A N D A D D R E S S I N G A L L P R E S E N T M
C K O N M E S H E A D D E D T U R N I N G T O H E R H O
P T I O N A N D J U S T S E E H O W B A D L Y I A M D R
W A I S T E D L A C E T R I M M E D D A I N T Y G R A Y
R E A S T S O Y E Z T R A N Q U I L L E L I S E Y O U W
N N A P A V L O V N A Y O U K N O W S A I D T H E P R I
T U R N I N G T O A G E N E R A L M Y H U S B A N D I S
L M E W H A T T H I S W R E T C H E D W A R I S F O R S
I T I N G F O R A N A N S W E R S H E T U R N E D T O S
E L I G H T F U L W O M A N T H I S L I T T L E P R I N
T H E N E X T A R R I V A L S W A S A S T O U T H E A V
A C L E S T H E L I G H T C O L O R E D B R E E C H E S
R O W N D R E S S C O A T T H I S S T O U T Y O U N G M
L K N O W N G R A N D E E O F C A T H E R I N E S T I M
```

Figure 7. *War and Peace*, "Hitler/Nazi," puzzle step = 69, "Hitler" step = 3, "Nazi" step = 207.

to verify manually, since it has a relatively small step of 40. The puzzle itself is 41 characters wide, so the rightmost column is a repetition of the leftmost. I used the computer to find several diagonal messages here: "Deer," "Regis," "Nazi," "Leno," "Dole." Many vertical messages were simple enough to be found just by poring over the puzzle: for example, "Oprah," "here," "Leia," "Hale," "sent," "nude," "pure," "hate," "data," "Roe," "Reed," "Meg," "hood," "pins (snip)," "Deion," and "lone." "Newt" is in there too, but at an offbeat step that makes for a jilted arrangement. And then, there are all those horizontal words too!

I suspect that with diligence, one could find enough matches to make almost all of the characters in the puzzle parts of hidden words. The puzzle below is rife with additional hidden surprises. Rips himself appears in "spirit" read backwards. "Pour," "Alan," and "sash" run vertically. And diagonal messages of varying complexity lurk everywhere. Can you find the "apes" swinging between "data" and "Reed"? "Love" intersecting with "nude"? How about "Ares," "reel," "deft," "lion," "dogs," "pony," "hard," "diet," "trace," "card," "Poe," and "wart"? They are all in there—and more.

There are dozens of linked messages in the puzzle. But how are we to know which words are linked by the secretive author? Is the "real" message "Nazi sent pure hate here," or is it "Deion pins nude Oprah?" All of these hits are authentic, encoded names that have lurked inside the text of the King James Version of Genesis for hundreds of years. But the whimsical combinations they appear in show that these surprises are simply lucky breaks, and not authentic messages from above.

```
T H E E A W A Y W I T H M I R T H A N D W I T H S O N G S W I T
A U G H T E R S T H O U H A S T N O W D O N E F O O L I S H L Y
R F A T H E R S P A K E U N T O M E Y E S T E R N I G H T S A Y
N O W T H O U G H T H O U W O U L D E S T N E E D S B E G O N E
A S T T H O U S T O L E N M Y G O D S A N D J A C O B A N S W E
```

Figure 8a. Step matrix for Genesis, "Roswell/UFO," step = 88.

```
A L L T H E R I C H E S W H I C H G O D H A T H T A K E N F R O
R E T H R E N W I T H H I M A N D P U R S U E D A F T E R H I M
E R S T H O U H A S T N O W D O N E F O O L I S H L Y I N S O D
E R V A N T S T E N T S B U T H E F O U N D T H E M N O T T H E
E N T Y Y E A R S H A V E I B E E N W I T H T H E E T H Y E W E
```

Figure 8b. Step matrix for Genesis, "Roswell/UFO/UFO," step = 589.

```
K A N D S A I D U N T O T H E M I S E E Y O U R F A T H E R
L T H A T L A B A N D O E T H U N T O T H E E I A M T H E G
O L D H I M N O T T H A T H E F L E D S O H E F L E D W I T
G H T E R S T H O U H A S T N O W D O N E F O O L I S H L Y
H E D A L L T H E T E N T B U T F O U N D T H E M N O T A N
```

Figure 8c. Step matrix for Genesis, "Roswell/UFO/IFO," step = 753.

```
U S A L I T T L E F O O D A N D J U D A H S P A K
E R E D S U R E L Y N O W W E H A D R E T U R N E
N D T H E M E N W E R E A F R A I D B E C A U S E
R A N D T H E Y M A D E R E A D Y T H E P R E S E
E E G Y P T I A N S M I G H T N O T E A T B R E A
B Y I N D E E D H E D I V I N E T H Y E H A V E D
R O U N D A N D J O S E P H S A I D U N T O T H E
E S A I D U N T O M Y L O R D T H E L A D C A N N
A N T S S H A L L B R I N G D O W N T H E G R A Y
```

Figure 9. Step matrix for Genesis, first "Regis" at step = 808, second "Regis" at step = 810 (puzzle step = 809).

```
S S E R V A N T S C A N W E F I N D S U C H A O N E A S T H I S I S A M A N I N W
W H O M T H E S P I R I T O F G O D I S A N D P H A R A O H S A I D U N T O J O S
S E P H F O R A S M U C H A S G O D H A T H S H E W E D T H E E A L L T H I S T H
H E R E I S N O N E S O D I S C R E E T A N D W I S E A S T H O U A R T T H O U S
S H A L T B E O V E R M Y H O U S E A N D A C C O R D I N G U N T O T H Y W O R D
D S H A L L A L L M Y P E O P L E B E R U L E D O N L Y I N T H E T H R O N E W I
I L L I B E G R E A T E R T H A N T H O U A N D P H A R A O H S A I D U N T O J O
O S E P H S E E I H A V E S E T T H E E O V E R A L L T H E L A N D O F E G Y P T
T A N D P H A R A O H T O O K O F F H I S R I N G F R O M H I S H A N D A N D P U
U T I T U P O N J O S E P H S H A N D A N D A R R A Y E D H I M I N V E S T U R E
E S O F F I N E L I N E N A N D P U T A G O L D C H A I N A B O U T H I S N E C K
K A N D H E M A D E H I M T O R I D E I N T H E S E C O N D C H A R I O T W H I C
C H H E H A D A N D T H E Y C R I E D B E F O R E H I M B O W T H E K N E E A N D
D H E M A D E H I M R U L E R O V E R A L L T H E L A N D O F E G Y P T A N D P H
H A R A O H S A I D U N T O J O S E P H I A M P H A R A O H A N D W I T H O U T T
T H E E S H A L L N O M A N L I F T U P H I S H A N D O R F O O T I N A L L T H E
E L A N D O F E G Y P T A N D P H A R A O H C A L L E D J O S E P H S N A M E Z A
A P H N A T H P A A N E A H A N D H E G A V E H I M T O W I F E A S E N A T H T H
H E D A U G H T E R O F P O T I P H E R A H P R I E S T O F O N A N D J O S E P H
H W E N T O U T O V E R A L L T H E L A N D O F E G Y P T A N D J O S E P H W A S
S T H I R T Y Y E A R S O L D W H E N H E S T O O D B E F O R E P H A R A O H K I
```

Figure 10. Genesis 41:38–46, multiple matches, step = 40.

What Are the Odds, Really?

Drosnin and his colleagues say that getting linked matches by coincidence is statistically impossible and cite the odds against such coincidences as more than 3,000 to 1 (and sometimes *much* more). Using numbers like these, the Bible code promoters try to convince their readers that the existence of God is now proven statistically *beyond the shadow of a doubt,* simply because they can find linked pairs like "Clinton" and "chief" in the same general area of the Bible.

But their core conclusions are based on severely flawed probability arguments. Drosnin's formulation of the improbability of the occurrence of linked pairs is implicitly based on the assumption that you have only one opportunity to get the match. But, with the help of the computer, Drosnin gets to take advantage of *billions* of opportunities.

Let's look at Drosnin's approach with a lottery analogy. The probability of winning a lottery with a single ticket is very small, and Drosnin says the probability of getting an improbable match (such as "Clinton" and "president") is also very small. But what happens if you buy more than one ticket?

In the New Mexico "Daily Millions" lottery, the odds of winning the $1 million jackpot with just one ticket are about ten million to one against. With two tickets, the odds plummet, to about five million to one. If you buy one million tickets, your odds drop to only about ten to one against. And if you invest $10 million in tickets, the odds become approximately two to one in your favor! Most people can't afford to buy millions of tickets. Those who *do* have that kind of money usually don't dump it on the lottery, because you almost always end up losing.

But in Drosnin's game, you don't have to win more than you lose. You don't even have to break even. All you need for success is to win *every once in a while*. And, you can have what amounts to millions of "free lottery tickets" simply by running a computer program, or poring over crossword-puzzle printouts. Drosnin routinely tests *billions* of letter sequences for matches to selected words or names, and goes to steps of many thousands. By using steps lower than 1,000 only, I limited myself to using only about 3 percent of the potential of Genesis or *Edwards*. Brendan McKay (in personal communication) showed me how to find hidden words much more efficiently, and a search of KJV Genesis at all possible steps for my list of twenty-five names came up with over one million additional matches. These include six hits for "Clinton," fifteen for "Gardner," three for "Hillary" and "Einstein," and two for "Kennedy."

Conclusion

The promoters of hidden-message claims say, "How could such amazing coincidences be the product of random chance?" I think the real question should be, "How could such coincidences *not* be the inevitable product of a huge sequence of trials on a large, essentially *random* database?"

Once I learned how to navigate in puzzle-space, finding "incredible" predictions became a routine affair. I found "comet," "Hale," and "Bopp" linked in KJV Genesis, along with "forty" and "died," which could be interpreted as an obvious reference to Heaven's Gate. I found "Trinity," "Los Alamos," "atom," and "bomb" encoded together in *Edwards,* in a section containing references to "security," "test," and "anti-fascist." And I found "Hitler" linked to "Nazi" dozens of times in several books. When I set out to engineer a "hidden code" link of "code" and "bogus" in KJV Genesis, I was able to produce sixty closely linked pairs. And every single one of these pairs could fit inside a reasonably sized puzzle.

The source of the mysterious "Bible code" has been revealed—it's *homo sapiens.* Now somebody go tell Oprah.

References

Begley, Sharon. 1997. Seek and ye shall find. *Newsweek,* June 9, pp. 66–67.
Drosnin, Michael. 1997. *The Bible Code.* New York: Simon and Schuster.
Gardner, Martin. 1997. Farrakhan, Cabala, Baha'i, and 19. *Skeptical Inquirer* 21 (2): 16–18, 57.
Hewitt, V. J., and Peter Lorie. 1991. *Nostradamus: The End of the Millennium.* New York: Simon and Schuster.

Hoagland, Richard C., 1992. *The Monuments of Mars: A City on the Edge of Forever.* Berkeley, Calif.: North Atlantic Books.

Van Biema, David. 1997. Deciphering God's plan. *Time,* June 9, p. 56.

Witztum, Doron, Eliyahu Rips, and Yoav Rosenburg. 1994. Equidistant letter sequences in the Book of Genesis. *Statistical Science* 9 (3).

Superstition and the Regression Effect

by JUSTIN KRUGER, KENNETH SAVITSKY, and THOMAS GILOVICH

What do actors David Duchovny, Ben Affleck, and Matthew McConaughey have in common? Fame. Fortune. A penchant for science fiction films about the apocalypse. And oh yes—each has been cursed.

Consider the evidence. A recent issue of *Newsweek* noted that each actor has been featured in a different periodical in what could be mistaken for identical photographs. The shots of *X-Files* star David Duchovny (appearing in *Us* magazine) and *Armageddon*'s Ben Affleck (in *GQ*) bear an uncanny resemblance to a photo of *Contact* star Matthew McConaughey that appeared some time ago in *Vanity Fair,* when he was widely touted as the "hot" new actor on the Hollywood scene.

And indeed, there is a resemblance: All three actors can be seen in nearly identical poses, sprawled across the front seats of old pickup trucks in jeans, rumpled shirts, and meticulously tousled hair. But it was not this eerie similarity that caught our eye. Instead, it was a warning offered by *Newsweek* to Duchovny and Affleck: "In his post-pickup phase," the article notes, McConaughey "has sometimes had a difficult time pleasing the critics" (Sigesmund 1998, 91).

The implication of the warning, presumably, is that Duchovny and Affleck should take heed of the fact that McConaughey's rise to fame became somewhat less meteoric following the publication of his pickup-truck photo. Furthermore, the insinuation is that the photograph may have had something to do with it— and that the same thing could happen to the other two.

To be sure, *Newsweek* offered its warning in jest. With a few notable exceptions, one's fame is unlikely to be affected by activities in the front seat of an automobile. But it is the case that film critics lost some of their taste for McConaughey shortly after his photo appeared in print—no longer is he Hollywood's "golden boy." And what is more, we confidently predict that a similar fate is likely to befall the other two actors. They too will likely find their celebrity fleeting. Importantly, however, we base our prediction not on any "pickup-truck curse," but on a mathematical truism known as the *regression effect*.

The Regression Effect

In the late nineteenth century, Sir Francis Galton conducted a rather uninteresting study that just happened to produce a result "of timeless significance" (Edwards 1993, 96). Galton was interested in the relationship between the heights of fathers and their sons. The uninteresting part is that he found one: Tall fathers have taller sons than do short fathers. (Of course, the same holds true for fathers and daughters, as well as for mothers and their children.) Galton's correlation was less than perfect, but it was there, just as expected.

But Galton also noticed something quite unexpected (Edwards 1993). Despite the strong relationship between the heights of fathers and sons, the tallest fathers tended to have sons that were somewhat shorter than the fathers themselves (Galton 1885). Likewise, the shortest fathers had sons who, although short, were a bit taller than they were. Why this curious attenuation? As it turns out, it *has* to be true.

To see why, it is necessary to recall that height, like many things, is multi-determined. One reason people are tall is because they have inherited the genetic predisposition to be tall, hence Galton's initial finding. But height is not purely a genetic affair, and even its genetic component is not controlled by a single gene. A person's height, after all, is determined by such disparate physical features as the height of the forehead, the length of the shinbone, and the size of each vertebra. For a person to be unusually tall or short, then, a great number of things must fall into place. A very tall person must acquire the gene from the right parent for each of these physical features, as well as receive a healthy diet, plenty of exercise, and freedom from growth-stunting pathogens. Scientists refer to the contribution of all of these hard-to-prophesize elements as "random error."

What Galton recognized was that extremely tall people tend to have random error working in their favor. That is, they are tall not simply because their parents were tall, but also because they got just the right combination of genes from their parents, were well nourished as children, led healthy lives, and so on. Of course, the children of these very tall people will, in turn, benefit from a tall gene pool, but random error is unlikely to work so well in their favor. The genetic "lottery" is unlikely to award them the favorable parental gene for as many physical features, and their childhood experiences are unlikely to be as kind. The net result is that, on average, they will be shorter than their parents. (The logic is reversed for extremely short parents.)

This is the regression effect: When two variables are imperfectly related, extreme values—high or low—on one of the variables tend to be matched by less extreme values on the other. As a consequence, very tall fathers tend to have

tall children, but not as tall (on average) as they are themselves; high school vale-
dictorians tend to do well in college, but not as well (on average) as they did in
high school; a company's disastrous years tend to be followed by more profitable
ones, and its banner years by those that are less profitable.

What does all this have to do with Duchovny, Affleck, and McConaughey?
Think of the week-to-week fluctuations in an actor's fame—exemplified by gossip
columnists' relentless listings of "who's hot and who's not"—as analogous to the
fluctuations in height over successive generations. To focus on those celebrities
who happened to have their pictures featured in national magazines (whatever the
pose) is like considering only the tallest of parents: In both cases, one has sampled
from the upper tail of the distribution. The three actors in question each had
their pictures featured (as is typically the case) when they were particularly
newsworthy—i.e., when their careers were at a peak. And since an actor's
popularity at different moments in time is imperfectly correlated (there is more
than a little random error there, to be sure), one can predict by regression alone
that an extraordinarily "hot" moment will be followed, on average, by a somewhat
less extraordinarily hot moment, just as an extraordinarily tall parent tends to be
followed, on average, by a somewhat less extraordinarily tall son or daughter.

Thus, the *Newsweek* warning may be right—but for the wrong reason. A slip
in Duchovny's or Affleck's popularity is likely, not because of any pick-up truck
curse, but because of the regression effect.

Although the regression effect is easy to grasp, people often have difficulty
spotting its influence in everyday life. This can result in a variety of superstitious
beliefs, from the benign to the pernicious. We review a sample of these in the
remainder of this article. Consider, first, three examples from the world of sports.

Regression Effects in the Sports World

Professional athletes are not known to shy away from celebrity. And yet, when
it comes to having their picture featured on the cover of *Sports Illustrated* magazine, a surprising number would happily go without. Why the sudden mod-
esty? Many athletes and fans alike believe that it is bad luck to be featured on
the cover of that particular publication. Despite the prestige, they fear that it
will spell doom for whatever athletic success was responsible for getting them or
their team on the cover in the first place. Swimmer Shirley Babashoff, for example, reportedly balked at having her picture taken for *Sports Illustrated* before the
1976 Olympics because she was afraid she would be jinxed (Gilovich 1991).
(She was eventually persuaded to pose when reminded that a cover story on
Mark Spitz had not prevented him from winning seven gold medals in the previous Olympic games. Babashoff herself went on to take home five medals.)

It does not take much statistical sophistication to see how regression effects
may be responsible for the so-called *"Sports Illustrated* jinx." As is the case with an

actor's popularity, an athlete's performances from time to time are imperfectly correlated, resulting from a mixture of true talent, situational factors, and random error. Thus, due to regression alone, one can expect an outstanding performance to be followed, on average, by a somewhat less outstanding performance. And since athletes, like actors, tend to appear on the covers of magazines when they are at a peak, an athlete's superior performance in the weeks preceding a cover story is likely to be followed by somewhat poorer performance in the weeks after. The supernatural is invoked to explain what simple mathematics handles quite nicely.

Consider another example, this time from the world of baseball. A player is called up from the minor leagues and has a brilliant rookie year in the majors, only to slip in his second season. This scenario is so familiar that it even has a name: the "sophomore slump" (Nisbett and Ross 1980).

Is the sophomore slump real? If one examines statistics such as batting-averages, fielding errors, and runs-batted-in, it becomes clear that it is not: There is no overall tendency for a major leaguer's performance to be lower in his second season than in his first. On the other hand, there is a tendency for *certain* players to experience a mysterious "slump" in their sophomore season. Any guesses as to which? It is those who had the most exceptional rookie seasons—those whose success was probably augmented by some amount of random error, and whose performance can be expected to decline, due to regression alone, in their second year.[1]

If there is no such thing as an overall sophomore slump, why does the myth persevere? Psychologist Saul Kassin suggests it is because baseball fans are not unlike the editors of *Sports Illustrated*. Just as the magazine preferentially selects the most exceptional athletes to feature on its cover, fans tend to think about and remember those players who have had the most exceptional rookie years. One remembers the dazzling debuts of Vida Blue, Mark Fidrych, and Fernando Valenzuela, for example, but not the hum-drum inaugural seasons of other, less celebrated rookies. Thus, belief in the sophomore slump results from a tendency of fans to spontaneously select instances from the upper tail of the distribution, and then to fail to realize that the exceptional performances of these players are likely to regress in their second seasons.

A final example from the world of sports involves a sure-fire cure for a team's poor win-loss record: Fire the coach in mid-season and start afresh. (Indeed, for some teams, the firing and hiring of coaches is a sport unto itself!) And it works. Kassin found that baseball teams that fire their managers in mid-season win a greater proportion of their games after the change in leadership than before. But is it necessarily the case that a new manager *causes* the improvement? To be sure, there are undoubtedly cases in which the dismissal of an incompetent manager does have a causal effect on the team's level of play. But the same improvement can just as easily be accounted for by regression.

Once again, consider the circumstances that are likely to surround a team's decision to switch managers. Seldom, of course, would a team consider such dire action when things are going well, nor even when things are going only somewhat poorly. Firing the manager is a tactic that is reserved for exceptionally poor performance. And since a team's performance from game to game and year to year is correlated (most of the players are the same, after all)—but imperfectly so—a less abysmal record is almost sure to follow.

Superstition and Gambling

In 1992 alone, Americans wagered over $19.4 billion in Nevada and Atlantic City casinos. They got only $16.3 billion of it back (Christiansen 1993). This is, of course, by design: All casino games are games of chance with the odds virtually always in favor of the "house"—and against the gambler. As a result, there are very few "winners" in casino gambling (unless, of course, you count the casinos). To make matters worse, these losses come at an especially great cost to a large proportion of gamblers who are at or below the poverty line (Borg, Mason, and Shapiro 1990).

The interesting thing about gambling is that gamblers *know* the odds are stacked against them. Well, sort of. Psychologists have long noted that people's expectancies for personal success in chance situations are often higher than the objective probabilities warrant (e.g., Langer 1975; Golin, Terrell, and Johnson 1977). For instance, gamblers are more confident in their chances of winning when they themselves roll the dice than when a croupier rolls for them, and they are more confident when given the opportunity to "practice." Craps players may realize that the objective likelihood of rolling a "natural eight" is 1 in 36, but may nevertheless "feel" as if it is higher.

One reason for this is that gamblers, even very experienced ones, subscribe to a number of superstitions about things they can do to improve their odds (Carroll 1998; Henslin 1967). Blow on the dice before you throw them to improve your luck. Concentrate on the number you want to get in order to achieve your desired roll. Throw the dice with the left hand to turn an unlucky streak around, or, odder still, get up and walk around your chair three times.

It should come as no surprise that such techniques are wholly ineffective. But it is easy to see how a perfectly rational person might come to believe otherwise. A strategy that a player adopts after a run of "poor luck" (such as throwing the dice with the left hand or blowing on the dice) will appear to be effective, not because it is, but because one's luck is unlikely to remain poor forever. Eventually, a string a poor outcomes will regress in the positive direction. Of course, the probability of a win is not directly affected by previous wins and losses, but if one's initial performance is poor enough, improvement is almost assured. After four lost bets on the roulette wheel, for example, the odds of improvement in the next four spins is 95 percent. Thus, a gambler will see his or her performance "improve" regardless of the strategy he or she adopted—whether it was concentrating on a particular number, blowing on the dice, or spitting on the dealer. Note that this example is different from the others we have presented. In each case thus far, the various outcomes have been correlated: A father's height is related to his son's, a baseball player's performance in his rookie season is usually a good indicator of his performance in his second year, and a celebrity's fame at one time is correlated with his or her fame at another. In gambling, however, each roll of the dice or flip of the coin is an independent event, unaffected by the previous outcome. As a result, one can expect the amount of regression, and the misunderstandings that go along with it, to be even greater.[2]

Everyday Beliefs

Lest one think such erroneous beliefs are unique to desperate gamblers or thoughtless sports fans, consider a more common superstition, one that rings true even for, well, us. Many people subscribe to the belief that calling attention to one's successes (even privately) is a sure way to invite disaster. Indeed, certain rituals have evolved to quell the anxiety that people feel in such situations (Ferm 1959). The pronouncement that the family vacation has thus far gone off without a hitch, the baby hasn't cried all day, or the stock market is on a roll, is likely to send many individuals scrambling for a piece of wood to knock.

How does regression contribute to this belief? By definition, such activity is likely to occur only when things are going well—the very time at which one's circumstances can be expected to regress and take a turn for the worse. Reflecting on one's good fortune does not cause the decline, of course, it merely co-occurs with it. In science, the mantra "correlation does not imply causation" protects against mistakenly inferring cause from co-occurrence. Everyday causal inference, however, even among those trained in statistics, is often far less sophisticated (Kelly 1967; Quattrone and Tversky 1984).

Or consider the popular wisdom among fans of the cinema that a sequel is rarely, if ever, as good as the original. We have little doubt that this observation is true. Whether one's measure is artistic merit or box office revenue, sequels are seldom the equals of their predecessors. To be sure, there are exceptions. Many film critics consider *Godfather II* to be as good as the original (e.g., Pauline Kael 1982), and several James Bond films have grossed more (even after correcting for inflation) than the original *Doctor No*. But examples of "sequel regression" are far easier to come by. *Star Wars* grossed far more than its sequels, as did *The Addams Family, Batman, City Slickers, Fletch, Free Willy, Home Alone, Jaws, Jurassic Park, Saturday Night Fever, Speed,* and dozens of others. Furthermore, virtually all of these films received more critical acclaim than their respective sequels.

What accounts for this trend? Avid moviegoers are quick to provide numerous explanations. Film studios may devote fewer resources to the script of a sequel, relying on patrons to buy tickets because of the quality of the original. Furthermore, some of a film's quality can derive from its novelty and original- ity. To the extent that a sequel capitalizes on the same basic formula as the orig- inal, then, viewers are likely to feel as if they've "been there, done that." These and other factors doubtless play a role in the typical slide in quality from origi- nal to sequel. But notice that regression alone would produce such a trend even if sequels were given the most lavish budgets and studios were not so compla- cent the second time around. After all, there is bound to be some random error in which movies garner critical acclaim and box office success. And since it is typically the most successful movies—ones that have likely capitalized on this random error—that are made into sequels, some regression is inevitable.

Alternative Medicine

Perhaps the most tragic instances of misunderstood regression come from a domain all too familiar to the readers of *Skeptical Inquirer*: the fringes of alter- native medicine. Time and time again, intelligent, rational people undergo med- ical treatments of unproven efficacy. Ginseng, for example, has been advertised nationally as able to improve physical performance and mental alertness, despite data to the contrary (Bahrke and Morgan 1994). Shark cartilage is consumed with alarming frequency, based on the questionable logic that, since sharks do not get cancer, consumption of their cartilage ought to provide the same resis- tance (Lane and Comac 1992; 1996). As it happens, sharks *do* get cancer, as Lane and Comac reluctantly admit (1996, 25), but that has not quelled a seven- fold increase in the commercial slaughter of sharks in some areas as a result of the fad (NCAHF 1993). Herbalist Hulda Regehr Clark suggests a somewhat more benign treatment (for sharks, at least): She recommends a concoction of black walnut hulls, wormwood capsules, and ground cloves as a cure for both cancer *and* AIDS, according to her self-published book *The Cure For All Cancers*.

At best, these treatments are ineffective. At worst, they are dangerous. The herbal cure-all *ma huang*, for example, has caused numerous deaths, as has the recent trend of coffee enemas, said to treat cancer and other diseases by "detox- ifying" the body (Kolata 1996). The National Heart, Lung and Blood Institute has documented several cases of kidney failure and death in people who have undergone "chelation therapy," the intravenous injection of the synthetic chelat- ing agent EDTA, advertised as a treatment for such diverse ailments as heart dis- ease, Parkinson's, Alzheimer's, and sexual impotence. And in addition to these direct harms, such "cures" wreck havoc indirectly, since individuals may aban- don more proven curative techniques in favor of alternative approaches.[3]

Given this track record, why are so many people convinced that these regimens work? One answer has less to do with *which* therapy an individual pursues than *when* he or she pursues it. As Beyerstein (1997) notes, many diseases are inherently cyclical—they have their "ups and downs." It is no great leap to assume that patients who seek alternative therapies do not do so arbitrarily, but when they have "hit rock bottom." Understandably so: desperate times call for desperate measures. But the timing of such desperate action is likely to contribute to erroneous beliefs about the effectiveness of the remedies they try. Not unlike the baseball team that fires its manager in the midst of a slump and subsequently experiences an upswing in its performance, moments when one's medical condition flares up (and one happens to appeal to an alternative therapy) are likely to be followed by moments of relative relief. Thus, just as a change in a team's management can appear to have done the trick, a bogus therapy can seem effective, even when it is not.[4]

Note that the regression effect can apply just as readily to beliefs about conventional medicine. Take, for example, the common notion that a diet low in saturated fat can reduce one's serum cholesterol level. It can—but not as much as is commonly believed (Moore 1989). This exaggerated faith in the benefits of a low-fat diet is understandable, however, in light of when people change their diet.[5] One can most easily be coaxed into lowering one's intake of cheeseburgers and french fries after a test reveals an exceptionally high cholesterol level. But such an exceptional result is likely to be due, at least in part, to random error. Thus, when one is tested again, after weeks or months on a restricted diet, one is likely to get a lower result. To be sure, the change may be bolstered by changes in one's diet, but random error is unlikely to augment one's result as much as before. Thus, regression makes the causal relationship between treatment and cure appear stronger than it is.

Concluding Remarks

"It's getting better all the time. (It couldn't get no worse.)"
—John Lennon and Paul McCartney

We have discussed a number of superstitious and misguided beliefs that arise from a misunderstanding of statistical regression. Notice, however, that individuals are not wholly wrong in their predictions. In many cases, the predictions people make are quite accurate: Athletes or celebrities may well experience a lull in their careers immediately after being pictured on a magazine cover, exceptional ballplayers often do go south in their second seasons, teams that fire their managers do subsequently perform better, and one may in fact experience an abatement of one's symptoms after trying an alternative medical therapy.

Thus, the error that individuals make is not one of *prediction,* but *explanation.* Elaborate causal scenarios that appeal to all manner of mystical, pseudoscientific, or otherwise superfluous beliefs are constructed to explain what is a simple mathematical given. One may be well advised to remember that when things get better, it is often, as Lennon and McCartney note, because they couldn't get much worse.

Acknowledgments

We thank Nick Epley and Tom Keegan for their helpful comments on an earlier draft of this article, and Saul Kassin for sharing his data with us.

Notes

1. Note that regression is likely to be something of a unidirectional phenomenon in this case. Although one might expect a "sophomore surge," on average, for those players who had exceptionally poor rookie seasons, such players are seldom asked back to the majors for a second year—or even make it all the way through their first. Indeed, this same asymmetry likely exists in a host of other domains, for analogous reasons. For example, professional musicians whose debut release is a flop are unlikely to land a second record deal, and businesses that turn in catastrophic losses in a particular year may be forced to close.

2. The amount of regression to be expected is inversely proportional to the magnitude of the correlation between the two variables. High correlation, less regression; low correlation, more correlation. In the extreme case of perfect association between two variables, there is *no* regression.

3. Worse still, those who utilize alternative therapies may come to ignore symptoms that indicate a need for medical attention. Indeed, patients may even be *instructed* to ignore such symptoms. The National Council Against Health Fraud (1996) notes that complaints of symptoms such as nausea, diarrhea, weakness, numbness, and tingling following herbal "detoxification" treatments are often ignored because salespeople falsely tell consumers that such symptoms are normal, and are due to the "cleansing" of the body.

4. It is for precisely this reason that clinical trials necessitate a placebo control group. Without one, it can be difficult to separate the effectiveness of the therapy from the natural course of the disease. Alternative medicines, because they are often classified as "dietary supplements," are not required to be tested in this manner by the Food and Drug Administration.

5. Another reason derives from what psychologists call the "representativeness heuristic," the notion that "like goes with like" (Kahneman and Tversky 1972; Gilovich and Savitsky 1996). Because the fat on the side of a steak or on the bottom of a skillet looks like it could clog arteries, one assumes that it does.

References

Bahrke, M. S., and Morgan, W. P. 1994. Evaluating the ergogenic properties of ginseng. *Sports Medicine* 18, 229–248.

Beyerstein, B. L. 1997. Why bogus therapies seem to work. Skeptical Inquirer 21, September/October 29–34.

Borg, M. O., P. M. Mason, and S. L. Shapiro. 1990. An economic comparison of gambling behavior in Atlantic City and Las Vegas. *Public Finance Quarterly* 18, 291–312.

Carroll, W. 1998. *Superstitions: 10,000 You Really Need.* San Diego, Calif.: SD Books.

Christiansen, E. M. 1993. 1992 gross annual wager: Industry rebounds with 8.4% handle gain. *Gaming and Wagering Business* 14, 12–35.

Edwards, A. W. F. 1993. Galton, Karl Pearson and modern statistical theory. In M. Keynes Ed., *Sir Francis Galton, FRS: The Legacy of His Ideas* (pp. 91–107). Houndmills, Basingstoke, Hampshire: Macmillan

Ferm, V. T. A. 1959. *A Brief Dictionary of American Superstitions.* New York: The Philosophical Library, Inc.

Galton, F. 1885. Regression towards mediocrity in hereditary stature. *Journal of the Anthropological Institute of Great Britain and Ireland* 15, 246–263.

Gilovich, T. 1991. *How We Know What Isn't So: The Fallibility of Human Reason in Everyday Life.* New York: Free Press.

Gilovich, T., and Savitsky, K. 1996. Like goes with like: The role of representativeness in erroneous and pseudoscientific beliefs. SKEPTICAL INQUIRER 20, March/April, 34–40.

Golin, S., T. Terrell, and B. Johnson. 1977. The illusion of control among depressed patients. *Journal of Abnormal Psychology* 88, 454–457.

Henslin, J.M. 1967. Craps and magic. *American Journal of Sociology* 73, 316–330.

Kael, P. 1982. *5001 Nights at the Movies: A Guide From A to Z.* New York: Holt, Rinehart and Winston.

Kahneman, D., and A. Tversky. 1972. Subjective probability: A judgment of representativeness. *Cognitive Psychology* 3, 430–454.

Kahneman, D., and A. Tversky. 1973. On the psychology of prediction. *Psychological Review* 80, 237–251.

Kelly, H.H. 1967. Attribution theory in social psychology. In D. Levine Ed., *Nebraska Symposium on Motivation* (Vol. 15, pp. 192–240). Lincoln, Neb.: University of Nebraska Press.

Kolata, G. 1996. On Fringes of Health Care, Untested Therapies Thrive. *The New York Times* June 17. p. A1, C11.

Lane, I.W., and L. Comac. 1992. *Sharks Don't Get Cancer.* New York: Avery.

Lane, I.W., and L. Comac. 1996. *Sharks Still Don't Get Cancer.* New York: Avery.

Langer, E. J. 1975. The illusion of control. *Journal of Personality and Social Psychology* 32, 311–328.

Moore, T.J. 1989. *Heart Failure: A Critical Inquiry into American Medicine and the Revolution in Heart Care.* New York: Random House, c1989.

National Council Against Health Fraud. 1993. *NCAHF Newsletter* Vol. 16, July/August. Loma Linda, Calif.: Author.

National Council Against Health Fraud. 1996. *NCAHF Newsletter* Vol. 19, March/April. Loma Linda, Calif.: Author.

Nisbett, R., and L. Ross. 1980. *Human Inference: Strategies and Shortcomings of Social Judgment.* Englewood Cliffs, New Jersey: Prentice-Hall.

Quattrone, G.A., and A. Tversky, 1984. Causal versus diagnostic contingencies: On self-deception and on the voter's illusion. *Journal of Personality and Social Psychology* 46, 237–248.

Sigesmund, B.J. 1998. Pinups pop up in pickups. *Newsweek* March 2. Hollywood scene.

Maria's Near-Death Experience
Waiting for the Other Shoe to Drop

by HAYDEN EBBERN, SEAN MULLIGAN, and BARRY L. BEYERSTEIN

I'm not afraid to die; I just don't want to be there when it happens.

—Woody Allen

Skeptics enter most debates at a disadvantage because they are usually forced to cast doubt on comforting beliefs. The idea that so-called near-death experiences, NDEs for short, could count as evidence for survival of the soul after death is perhaps the most comforting belief of all. Since physician Raymond Moody (1975) coined the term "near-death experience" to describe a reasonably consistent set of experiences recalled by about a third of those who are resuscitated after near-fatal incidents, such descriptions have been welcomed with enthusiasm by a large segment of the public.

Susan Blackmore (1991) has described near-death experience as follows: "For many experiencers, their adventures seem unquestionably to provide for evidence for life after death, and the profound effects the experience can have on them is just added confirmation. By contrast, for many scientists these experiences are just hallucinations produced by the dying brain and of no more interest than an especially vivid dream. So which is right? . . . neither is quite right: NDEs provide no evidence for life after death, and we can best understand them by looking at neurochemistry, physiology, and psychology; but they are much more interesting than any dream. . . . Any satisfactory theory . . . leads us to questions about minds, selves, and the nature of consciousness."

Historically, philosophers have used the term *mind* to refer to the subjective awareness of one's self and its surroundings and the experience of imagining, planning, and willing our actions. Psychologists and neuroscientists generally prefer the term *consciousness* when referring to this inner stream of perceptions, images, memories, and feelings. It is from them that the brain assembles the conscious model it experiences as reality. By mixing inference with sensory inputs, body images, emotions, and stored memories, the brain constructs our sense of an ongoing self dwelling in a physical body, surrounded by a real world of objects and events. In religious lore, the terms *soul* or *spirit* encompass not only this subjective awareness of the self and its whereabouts, but also the belief that this mental tableau is a manifestation of a divine *essence* each individual is thought to possess. Believers consider souls nonmaterial, usually immortal. In what follows, *mind* and *consciousness* will refer to secular, naturalistic depictions of mental awareness. *Soul* or *spirit* will be reserved for when the holder's views imply that this awareness of the self is somehow supernatural, separable from the body, and capable of surviving death (i.e., in an "afterlife"). NDEs are only one example of episodes in which the brain's construction of reality breaks down temporarily and allows the self model to *feel* as if it were pure spiritual essence, no longer attached to a physical body.

The NDE typically begins with a sense of serenity and relief, followed by a feeling that the self is leaving the body (the "out-of-body experience," or OBE). From this vantage point, the supposedly disembodied spirit sometimes feels that it is observing attempts to revive its lifeless body. A subset of those who reach the OBE stage further report being propelled through a spiral tunnel toward a bright light. For some, the light eventually resolves into a significant religious figure, deceased relative or friend, or vista of paradise. As rescue procedures begin to take effect, these patients often report feeling great reluctance at being pulled back into the painful, uncertain, everyday world.

Virtually every book retelling this now-familiar story achieves best-seller status and reaps substantial rewards for its author.

James Alcock (1981) provided several insights into the motivations underlying this fervent longing for "proof" of an afterlife. He also suggested an explanation for why the will to believe so readily overcomes the desire to examine the evidence critically (Alcock 1981, 65):

> Intellectually capable of foreseeing that they will one day die, yet emotionally too frail to accept that physical death may indeed be the end of their existence, human beings have long clung to the idea that life continues beyond the grave.

Alcock reminds us that survival beyond death lies at the core of almost all formal religions and that protecting this hope was also a major impetus for the founding of the modern discipline of parapsychology. Alcock was referring in the latter statement to the eminent group of British scholars and statesmen who in the nineteenth century banded together to form the Society for Psychical Research. Disturbed by the implications of modern science for their Christian worldview, these members of the intelligentsia espoused the goal of establishing *scientific* proof for the existence of an immortal soul.

Reports of NDEs appeared earlier than the nineteenth century, however. One of the earliest accounts is that of a soldier's supposed return from death, found in

Plato's *Republic.* The Bible too is replete with stories of people raised from the dead, as are the sacred texts of most other faiths. Although reports of NDEs have shown up over the centuries, the appearance rate seems to have increased dramatically in recent times. This is likely due to vast improvements in emergency medicine, coupled with a worldwide resurgence of religious fundamentalism (a twentieth-century movement among Christians, Jews, and Muslims that advocates the literal interpretation of their respective sacred writings). The spiritual interpretation of NDEs is reinforced by the mass media, which prosper by pandering to public longings of all sorts, including the desire for life after death.

The concept of immortality is, in the final analysis, a metaphysical proposition that can only be accepted or rejected on faith (Edwards 1992). While faith alone used to be sufficient to bolster such convictions, the growing prestige of science has left many sophisticated believers uneasy in the absence of more solid proof of an afterlife. In response, a field known as "near-death studies" has emerged with the thinly veiled agenda of providing a scientific gloss for religious views of an afterlife. About the same time, another field emerged known as "anomalistic psychology" (Reed 1988; Zusne and Jones 1989; Neher 1990). It accepts that experiences such as NDEs and OBEs can seem compellingly real to those who have them, but offers many reasons to doubt their reality outside the mind of the percipient (Blackmore 1993). Anomalistic psychology seeks naturalistic explanations for various seemingly supernatural states of consciousness based on sound psychological and neurophysiological research (Beyerstein 1987–1988, 1988).

To accept notions such as survival after death, disembodied spirits, and a host of other parapsychological phenomena, one must also adopt some form of the philosophical doctrine known as "dualism" (Beyerstein 1987–1988). Dualism asserts that the mind is fundamentally different from the physical body, and this is essentially equivalent to the religious concept of an "immaterial soul." If dualism is correct, it is possible, some say, for mind or consciousness to disengage temporarily from the body but still retain self-awareness and the ability to gather information and interact physically with the environment. Many dualists also believe that their spiritual selves are immortal and that these spiritual selves will eventually abandon their physical bodies and assume a separate existence in some other realm. All of this is impossible from the standpoint of "material monists" who assert that the mind is equivalent to and inseparable from brain function.

Not surprisingly, NDE accounts are welcomed by many occultists because they appear to be a major impediment to the materialist worldview they find so distasteful. Likewise, in fundamentalist circles, NDEs are hailed as a vindication for various spiritual teachings.

Materialists readily concede that the subjective experiences of the NDE *feel* very real. Indeed, they contend that NDEs helped suggest the concept of an immortal soul to our ancestors in the first place. Despite the subjective realness of the NDE, however, modern neuroscience offers not only a wealth of reasons to doubt the possibility of disembodied minds, but it also provides much evidence that the compelling subjective phenomena of the NDE can be generated by known brain mechanisms (Beyerstein 1988; Blackmore 1991, 1993). Believers counter that the NDE seems too real to have been a dream or hallucination, but they forget that what we *mean* by the term *hallucination* is an internally generated experience so detailed, emotional, and believable that it is indistinguishable from ordinary perceptions of reality (Siegel 1992; Beyerstein 1996).

It is also important to note that NDEs are always reported by people who presume they have died, but have not really died. Cardiopulmonary arrest (C.P.A.)—i.e., stoppage of the heart and lungs—was once an adequate definition of death. With the advent of modern resuscitation techniques, however, it became possible in some cases to restore breathing and pulse, often as long as several minutes after they had ceased. During C.P.A., the brain undergoes several biochemical and physiological changes, but by relying on its limited backup of stored oxygen and metabolic fuels, certain aspects of consciousness can be sustained, albeit in a somewhat degraded fashion. Thus, it is not surprising that there might be some residual memories from the time that one was dying, but not yet clinically dead.

That this minority of revived C.P.A. patients recall anything from the interval tells us more about how the brain creates our sense of self and the feeling that there is an external reality than it does about the possibility of an afterlife. Much can be learned from studying the orderly fashion in which these internally constructed models shut down when the brain is traumatized, but because those who have been revived did not reach the irreversible state of brain death, any experiences they recall cannot be said to have come from "the other side."

The subjective contents of the NDE are anything but unique to the onset of death. The basic elements of the NDE are common to hallucinations of various sorts. They are also found in psychedelic drug states, psychoses, and migraine and epileptic "auras" (Siegel 1992; Blackmore 1991, 1993; Beyerstein 1996). Similar experiences have even been reported in a surprisingly high proportion of those who panic during natural disasters, when they are psychologically traumatized but in no real physical danger (Cardeña and Spiegel 1993).

If the components of the NDE have plausible roots in brain physiology, this undermines the argument that they are a glimpse of the afterlife rather than a rich and believable hallucination. It is for this reason that accounts of NDEs that contain elements that are logically incompatible with the hallucination hypothesis assume special importance.

One attempt to gather objective evidence, rather than the usual anecdotal, after-the-fact accounts, has been initiated by the British psychiatrist Peter Fenwick (personal communication). He has placed messages written on paper on ledges, above eye level, in the operating rooms of the hospital where he works. If a surgical patient should have an NDE/OBE, then his or her spirit, which supposedly hovers far above the body, looking down on it, should be able to read the otherwise inaccessible messages and recall them when revived. As yet, no one has been able to provide this kind of objective evidence, which would admittedly create serious problems for the materialist position. In the absence of such proof, the spiritually inclined fall back on those NDE reports where things are "recalled" about the resuscitation environment, or about distant places that the revived person supposedly could not have known unless his or her spiritual self had been observing from outside the body.

Psychologist Ray Hyman has long urged his fellow skeptics to concentrate on the cases that supporters of paranormal claims put forth as their very best. If these examples fall short, logically or empirically, the remainder must be even weaker.

In the area of near-death studies, the widely cited story of the Seattle heart patient known as "Maria" occupies a place of pride for paranormalists (Clark 1984; Wilson 1987; Rogo 1989; Blackmore 1993; Ring and Lawrence 1993).

This account is held in such high regard primarily for two reasons. First, many of its proponents have some professional standing. More important, it is claimed that, during her NDE, Maria became aware of things, including an oddly positioned shoe, that were impossible for her to have known unless her spirit had literally departed and returned to her body. Throwing down the gauntlet to disbelievers, the prominent NDE researchers Ring and Lawrence (1993, 223) say this about the case:

> Assuming the authenticity of the account, which we have no reason to doubt, the facts of the case seem incontestable. Maria's inexplicable detection of that inexplicable shoe is a strange and strangely beguiling sighting of the sort that has the power to arrest the skeptic's argument in mid-sentence, if only by virtue of its indisputable improbability.

Because Maria's story was frequently recommended to us as their "best case" by those who believe NDEs are different from hallucinations, we decided to conduct our own investigation. In 1994, Hayden Ebbern and Sean Mulligan traveled to Seattle to visit the sites where the events surrounding Maria's NDE transpired and had several conversations with Kimberly Clark, who first reported the incident (Clark 1984). They also attended a meeting of the support group Clark founded for people who have had the NDE. Despite repeated efforts, including contacting media people who publicized the event, we were unable to locate Maria or anyone other than Clark who claimed to have had direct contact with Maria. Given the seriousness of the medical condition that led to her NDE, we assume Maria is no longer living. The following description of Maria's NDE is constructed from Clark's (1984) original report and from telephone and face-to-face conversations the authors had with Clark.

Maria's NDE

In April of 1977, Maria, a migrant worker from the Yakima area of Washington state, was visiting friends in Seattle when she suffered a severe heart attack. She was taken, at night, by paramedics to Harborview Medical Center where she was admitted to the coronary care unit. Kimberly Clark, a social worker, was randomly assigned to Maria to provide assistance with social and financial problems arising from her illness. Clark says she spent a considerable amount of time with Maria and was with her when, three days after her admission to the hospital, she suffered a cardiac arrest. Because Maria was being monitored closely, she was resuscitated quickly and her condition stabilized.

Later the same day, Clark returned to see Maria and found her quite distressed about what she had experienced during the recent emergency. Maria told Clark, "The strangest thing happened when the doctors and nurses were working on me. I found myself looking down from the ceiling at them working on my body." Clark was not immediately impressed by this for she realized that, like most people who have been exposed to television, movies, novels, and magazines, Maria could be expected to have known what would be happening during such a procedure. Maria had also been in the cardiac facility long enough to become familiar with its staff, equipment, and emergency routines. And, because hearing is one of the last senses to drop out as someone loses consciousness, she could have heard much that she seemed to know about her resuscitation when she later described the scene to Clark. Thus Clark initially leaned toward our position that Maria's account was a sincere recollection of visual and audio images that welled up from her memory during her cardiac arrest. However, as Maria elaborated further, Clark began to doubt her own initial assessment.

Clark began to be impressed when Maria told her of seeing chart paper streaming from the machines monitoring her vital signs, even though no one had talked about it while reviving her. More dramatically, Maria also said that she

Figure 2. The Harborview Medical Center Emergency Room entrance, showing the canopy and curved driveway. Maria's room was directly above the entrance.

became distracted by something over the emergency room driveway and suddenly found herself outside the building, as if she had just "thought herself" there. Maria also described the area around the emergency entrance, relating details such as that the doors opened inward, that the emergency entrance is reached by a one-way road, and that the road had a curve in it.

These details piqued Clark's interest because she knew Maria had arrived after dark and she thought it unlikely that she would have absorbed much knowledge of the approaches to the emergency area. Initially, Clark considered the possibility that, because the room Maria was assigned is above the emergency entrance, she might have looked out the window sometime in the three days prior to her NDE, and noticed the layout of the area below. However, Clark told us that she came to believe that these prosaic explanations were unlikely. She believes that Maria could not have seen the driveway area from her window because it is obscured by a canopy over the entrance (figure 2). And furthermore, Clark asserted, Maria had been restrained by various lines attaching her to the physiological monitors, making it doubtful she could leave her bed to look out the window.

Maria went on to describe being distracted again, this time by something on a third floor, outside window ledge at the north side of the hospital. Maria said she "thought her way" up to the object and discovered that it was a shoe. She described it as a large tennis shoe that was worn at the small toe and sitting with a shoelace tucked under the heel. Maria then asked Clark to search for the shoe as a way of verifying that her spirit had really been out of her body.

Clark went outside to see if she could make out the shoe from ground level, but said she couldn't see anything unusual in the suggested direction. She then returned inside, went upstairs in that wing, and began going through various patients' rooms, looking out the windows. She recalls the windows as being so narrow that she had to press her face against the glass, just

Figure 1. View from the ground outside Harborview Medical Center where the shoe Maria said she saw was located. In the background is the Smith Tower, where an NDE support group said one would have to be positioned to see a shoe on the medical center window edge.

to see the ledge at all. Eventually, by pressing her face tightly against the glass of one of the windows, Clark says, she was able to look down and see a tennis shoe on the ledge. This was a third floor window ledge of a patient's room on the west side of the hospital's north wing. The wing faces Puget Sound and a local landmark known as the Smith Tower (figure 1). People at the NDE support group the authors attended embellished this part of the story, claiming that the shoe was positioned so that one would have to have been in the Smith Tower, miles away, to be at the correct angle to see it; then, of course, it would have been much too small to recognize from that distance.

Although she had been able, with difficulty, to see the shoe from inside, Clark believed her view of it had differed from Maria's. That is because for Maria to have noticed that the side of the shoe next to the small toe was worn and that a shoelace was tucked under the heel, she would need to have viewed it from the opposite direction; i.e., looking from outside toward the building rather than from inside. Clark is adamant that these details of the shoe could not have been visible from inside the hospital. Clark retrieved the shoe, convinced that it offered irrefutable proof that Maria's spirit had indeed left her body and floated outside of the hospital during her cardiopulmonary arrest.

Do These Recollections Require a Spiritual Interpretation?

On the surface, certain aspects of Maria's story seem to defy naturalistic explanation. The leading NDE researchers Ring and Lawrence, quoted earlier, accept Clark's spiritualistic interpretation wholeheartedly, although they do admit that not everyone would agree. There are, of course, other plausible explanations for the key points that distinguish this case. Closer examination reveals that the story is much less impressive than it seems at first blush.

Clark was impressed by the fact that Maria recalled seeing chart paper streaming from monitoring apparatus while she was supposedly out of her body. But, as Clark admits, Maria could have been familiar with the hospital equipment and procedures. So, like other parts of typical NDEs, it is quite possible that this was merely a visual memory incorporated into the hallucinatory world that is often formed by a sensory-deprived and oxygen-starved brain. We know that the brain frequently tries to construct a substitute image of external reality from memory when traumatic changes temporarily deprive it of its normal sensory inputs (Blackmore 1993; Beyerstein 1996). Because this memory-derived imagery is the most complete and stable construct the brain can muster under the circumstances, it is accepted as reality for the moment.

Maria's description of the emergency entrance and driveway area may also seem extraordinary at first glance, but a bit of reflection upon standard hospital design suggests that Maria reported nothing more than what common sense would dictate. It would strike most people as logical that the doors of a hospital emergency room would open inward as it would be awkward for paramedics to have to negotiate doors that opened toward them as they rush patients, stretchers, wheelchairs, and other apparatus into the emergency room. In addition, Maria may have picked up more direct knowledge of the scene than she was aware of, for she had been brought into the hospital through this entrance.

The same weaknesses are apparent when we consider Maria's knowledge of the driveway. Although it was dark when Maria arrived, the area is well-lighted. Even if she hadn't been fully conscious and able to observe the scene as she was trundled through it (hospital officials would not confirm Maria's level of consciousness upon arrival), it only makes sense to require one-way traffic in such areas to facilitate the safe and orderly entrance and exit of speeding emergency vehicles. And recall that the room Maria occupied for three days prior to her NDE was immediately above the emergency entrance (figure 2). Giving Clark the benefit of the doubt when she suggests that never once did Maria catch a glimpse of the entrance area beneath her window, it is still not far-fetched to assume that she could have gained some sense of the traffic flow from the sounds of the ambulances coming and going. At night, reflections of vehicle lights could also supply similar clues, even to a bedridden patient.

While most parts of Maria's account are neither unique nor convincing, her sighting of the tennis shoe seems problematic for those who would explain her NDE as a hallucination. Clark has long maintained that the shoe was undetectable except from a vantage point outside of the hospital and above the third floor of the building. As part of our investigation, Ebbern and Mulligan visited Harborview Medical Center to determine for themselves just how difficult it

Figure 3. Close-up Harborview Medical Center third-floor window ledge and the investigator's shoe.

would be to see, from outside the hospital, a shoe on one of its third-floor window ledges. They placed a running shoe of their own at the place Clark described and then went outside to observe what was visible from ground level. They were astonished at the ease with which they could see and identify the shoe (figure 3).

Clark's claim that the shoe would have been invisible from ground level outside the hospital is all the more incredible because the investigators' viewpoint was considerably inferior to what Clark's would have been seventeen years earlier. That is because, in 1994, there was new construction under way beneath the window in question and this forced Ebbern and Mulligan to view the shoe from a much greater distance than would have been necessary for Clark. Figure 4 shows Mulligan in front of the construction fence that prevents the much closer access that would have been possible in 1977. It is from this position that the photo in figure 3 was taken.

The construction site had been, until 1994, a parking lot and patient recreation area. Thus, back in 1977, many people in this high-traffic area would have had the opportunity to get a better view of a shoe on the ledge than we had. If

we could see our shoe with such ease from a greater distance, it seems reasonable that many people who used the parking lot and recreation facility would have noticed one as well. When Ebbern and Mulligan returned to Seattle one week after placing the shoe on the third-floor ledge, the shoe had been removed, proving that it was also discernible to someone not specifically looking for it.

It is not a far-fetched notion to assume that anyone who might have noticed the shoe back in 1977 would have commented on it because of the novelty of its location. Thus, during the three days prior to her NDE, Maria could have overheard such a conversation among any of the doctors, nurses, patients, visitors, or other hospital staff who frequented this busy area. Memory researchers are well aware that people can hear snippets of

Figure 4. Author Sean Mulligan outside the medical center, with the investigators' shoe visible on a third-floor window ledge. Note the construction fence that prevents the even closer access that was possible around the time of Maria's NDE.

conversations outside their focal awareness and recall the contents in various forms, including visual images, even though they honestly believe they never encountered the information before. This is known as "cryptomnesia" (Zusne and Jones 1989, 138).

Let us suppose, for the moment, that no one noticed the original shoe in 1977 on the hospital ledge from outside the building. Would that rule out non-spiritualistic explanations for the contents of Maria's NDE? Not necessarily. According to Clark, it was nearly impossible to see the shoe from inside the building. She emphasized how difficult it was to find the shoe when Maria asked her to search for it: "I went up to the third floor and began going in and out of patients' rooms and looking out their windows, which were so narrow that I had to press my face to the screen, just to see the ledge at all."

When Ebbern and Mulligan visited the third-floor wards at Harborview, they did not find this to be the case at all. They easily placed their running shoe on the ledge from inside one of the rooms and it was clearly visible from various points within the room. There was no need whatsoever for anyone to press his or her face against the glass to see the shoe. In fact, one needed only to take a few steps into the room to be able to see it clearly. To make matters worse for Clark's account, a patient would not even need to strain to see it from his or her bed in the room. So it is apparent that many people inside as well as outside the hospital would have had the opportunity to notice the now-famous shoe, making it even more likely that Maria could have overheard some mention of it. The peculiarity of its position would almost certainly invite speculations about what kind of prankster or bungler could have been responsible.

Those who prefer the spiritualistic explanation of Maria's NDE also stress a number of details in her description of the shoe. Clark has repeatedly declared that the only way Maria could have known about the worn spots on the shoe and position of the shoelace was if she had been hovering outside the window— allegedly these details were undetectable from anywhere else. Having visited the scene ourselves, we determined that one did not need to be pressed against the glass to see the shoe, but we did find that by assuming that position it would have been easy to discern the additional details that so impressed Clark. Looking down from that angle at the shoe we placed on the ledge, we had no difficulty seeing the shoe's allegedly hidden outer side.

Thus we believe we have shown that it would not have been as difficult as Clark claims for Maria to have become aware of the shoe prior to her NDE. It would have been visible, both inside and outside the hospital, to numerous people who could have come into contact with her. It also seems likely that some of them might have mentioned it within earshot. But even if we assume that none of this occurred, there are other considerations that make this less than the air-tight case its proponents believe it is.

Memory and Interpretive Biases

Kimberly Clark is not a trained investigator and she did not publicly report the details of Maria's NDE until seven years after it occurred. It is quite possible that during this interval some parts of the story were forgotten and some details may have been interpolated. As Clark has not produced notes or recordings from her interviews with Maria, we have no way of knowing what leading questions Maria may have been asked, or what Maria might have "recalled" that did not fit and was dropped from the record. Research shows that we all have a confirmatory bias that leads us to recall and embellish information that supports our beliefs and to forget parts that do not. This is true both for individuals central to the event and for their supporters, especially when an oral account of the event becomes the subject of controversy and there is a need to defend one's credibility and point of view. Memory researchers call this tendency for stories to improve over time "sharpening and levelling." Details that support a story assume greater prominence, and details that might make the story less convincing fade.

In talking about her NDE, Maria could have unintentionally filled in inferred details to flesh out the story. Pressed for details by someone in a position of authority, this woman of modest status could easily have succumbed to what psychologists call "demand characteristics" and, quite innocently, filled in more than she knew from direct experience. Research shows that humans edit and shape memories in order to achieve a comprehensible and satisfying account of past events. Once Maria had reported a shoe sitting on an outside ledge, it would have been plausible to infer it was an old shoe—otherwise wouldn't the owner have taken the trouble to retrieve it? From this, it is only a small step to assume a worn toe, not unusual in an old shoe. That the shoelace was correctly described by Maria as tucked under the heel may also have been a later addition to a story that, as we have seen, is marked with memory distortions on Clark's part. As far as we were able to ascertain, Clark never photographed the shoe on the ledge. When Ebbern and Mulligan asked Clark about the current whereabouts of the shoe, Clark replied that she probably had it around somewhere, maybe in her garage, but that it would be too much trouble to look for it. This cavalier attitude toward the most important artifact in the field of near-death studies struck us as odd, given the almost mythic status this humble piece of footware has been accorded.

Perhaps in her excitement at discovering the shoe, and in her haste to retrieve it, Clark did not spend sufficient time analyzing and recording details of the situation, and now honestly misremembers how closely the facts matched Maria's account. Note, for example, that her assertions about the invisibility of the shoe are clearly exaggerated in her memory. The motivation to defend cherished or self-serving beliefs makes it easy for unintentional embellishments to creep into key accounts as they are retold. In our discussions with her, Clark exhibited obvious emotional commitment to the spiritual interpretation of Maria's story. She has become a minor celebrity because of her involvement with it and is writing yet another, potentially profitable, book on the subject. When Ebbern and Mulligan attended meetings of the support group Clark runs (which bills itself as devoted to scientific research into NDEs), they were struck by the revival-meeting atmosphere. The participants exhibited a conspicuous lack of scientific knowledge and low levels of critical thinking skills. They seemed quite unaware of how to mount a proper investigation of such incidents. The appeal throughout was strictly to faith. The few mildly critical questions the visitors raised were decidedly unwelcome.

Conclusion

Our investigation cannot prove that Maria's spirit did not leave her body and return, nor that Kimberly Clark's recollections and interpretations are wrong. It does, however, show that this case, often touted as the best in the area of near-death studies, is far from unassailable, as its proponents assert.

We have shown several factual discrepancies and plausible ways that Maria's supposedly unobtainable knowledge could have been obtained by quite ordinary means. On delving into this incident, we were first disappointed, then amused, that such a weak case should have achieved the importance it has been accorded. Ring and Lawrence (1993) certainly must have spoken in haste when they issued their challenge; for rather than "arrest[ing] the skeptic's argument in mid-sentence," investigation of Maria's story has shown us the naivete and the power of wishful thinking in the supposedly scientific area known as "near-death studies." Once again, it is apparent why Demosthenes cautioned, more than 2000 years ago, "Nothing is easier than self-deceit, for what each man wishes, that he also believes to be true."

References

Alcock, J.E. 1981. Pseudoscience and the soul. *Essence* 5(1): 65–76.

Beyerstein, B.L. 1987-1988. The brain and consciousness: Implications for psi phenomena. SKEPTICAL INQUIRER 12(2) (Winter): 163–173.

Beyerstein, B. L. 1988. Neuropathology and the legacy of spiritual possession. SKEPTICAL INQUIRER 12(3) (Spring): 248–262.

Beyerstein, B.L. 1996. Visions and hallucinations. In *The Encyclopedia of the Paranormal*, ed. by Gordon Stein. Buffalo, NY: Prometheus Books.

Blackmore, S. 1991. Near-death experiences: In or out of the body? SKEPTICAL INQUIRER 16(1) (Fall): 34–45.

Blackmore, S. 1993. *Dying to Live: Near-Death Experiences*. Amherst, N.Y.: Prometheus Books.

Cardeña, E. and D. Spiegel. 1993. Dissociative reactions to the Bay Area earthquake. *American Journal of Psychiatry* 150: 474–478.

Clark, K. 1984. Clinical interventions with near-death experiencers. In *The Near-Death Experience: Problems, Prospects, Prospectives*, ed. by B. Greyson and C.P. Flynn, pp. 242–255. Springfield, Ill.: Charles C. Thomas.

Edwards, P., ed. 1992. *Immortality*. New York: Macmillan.

Moody, R.A. 1975. *Life after Life.* New York: Bantam.
Neher, A. 1990. *The Psychology of Transcendence.* New York: Dover.
Reed, G. 1988. *The Psychology of Anomalous Experience.* Amherst, N.Y.: Prometheus Books.
Ring, K. and M. Lawrence. 1993. Further evidence for veridical perception during near-death experiences. *Journal of Near Death Studies* 11: 223–229.
Rogo, D.S. 1989. *The Return from Silence.* Northamptonshire, U.K.: Aquarian Press.
Siegel, R.K. 1992. *Fire in the Brain: Clinical Tales of Hallucination.* New York: Plume/Penguin.
Wilson, I. 1987. *The After-Death Experience.* New York: William Morrow.
Zusne, L. and W.H. Jones 1989. *Anomalistic Psychology: A Study in Magical Thinking.* (2d ed.) Hillsdale, N.J.: Lawrence Erlbaum.

Secrets of a Russian Psychic

by MASSIMO POLIDORO

For years, psychic research in the USSR, owing to the aura of secrecy that surrounded it, has been regarded as some kind of myth. It was being said, for example, that the Russians were far ahead in parapsychological discoveries and that the West had better invest lots of money in the field to avoid a "psi-gap." The sparse information that reached the West hinted to extraordinary faculties being scientifically demonstrated by amazing psychics. During the early 1960s, interest in Soviet paranormal claims was first aroused by newspaper articles describing the astonishing abilities of Rosa Kuleshova, a twenty-two-year-old Russian girl who apparently could read print while blindfolded (*Time*, January 25, 1963; *Life*, June 12, 1964). However, the loose conditions in which Rosa operated allowed for very easy methods of deception to be used (Gardner 1981).

In 1968, films showing Nina Kulagina apparently moving objects with her mind (psychokinesis, or PK) were viewed at the First Moscow International Conference on Parapsychology and were also observed by some Western scientists. Finally, the general public became aware of the varied work in parapsychology carried out in the USSR with the publication of Sheila Ostrander and Lynn Schroeder's *Psychic Discoveries Behind the Iron Curtain* (1970), followed by various other similar publications on the subject.

Many films of Russian psychics at work have now been seen on Western television shows and documentaries. The most popular are those that show apparent PK in action. We have seen, then, Nina Kulagina apparently moving compass needles and light objects, Boris Ermolaev "levitating" small objects, and Alla Vinogradova willing round objects to roll on flat surfaces.

Russian PK Stars

As for Nina Kulagina, the conditions under which she operated were far from acceptable by basic scientific standards. Tests were frequently carried out at her own home or in hotel rooms; no tight controls were ever applied, owing in part to the fact that a demonstration might take several hours of preparation (i.e., concentration by Nina), which, of course, was no guarantee of success. Also, when watching these films, anybody who has a background in magic cannot avoid the feeling that she is using standard conjuring techniques: magnets hidden on her body to move the compass needle; threads or thin hair to move objects across the table; small mirrors concealed in her hand to read signs with numbers and letters being held behind her. Unfortunately, no expert in conjuring techniques was ever present at Kulagina's demonstrations.

Boris Ermolaev, a Russian film director, became relatively famous during the 1970s for his apparent ability to suspend objects in midair by concentrating on them. Ermolaev didn't perform on stage but showed his demonstrations *"only to serious scientists of his own choosing or to close friends"* (italics mine, Gris and Dick 1986). He and others were tested by Professor Venyamin Pushkin, who stated: "The experiments were conducted under the strictest controls, and no devices of any kind were used" (ibid.). However, in a 1992 *World of Discovery* documentary called "Secrets of the Russian Psychics," Ermolaev's method was finally revealed. He used to sit on a chair and then place the objects to be suspended between his knees; unfortunately for him, the light conditions when the documentary crew was filming were probably not what he was accustomed to. That's how the TV crew was able to capture a fine thread fixed at both his knees to which he attached the objects; the whole unmasking procedure was filmed and shown during the documentary.

Alla Vinogradova is another story.

Vinogradova's Moving Objects

A child psychologist and teacher, wife of Russian psi-researcher Victor Adamenko, Alla Vinogradova saw in 1969 a film of Kulagina in action and suspected that she too could move objects without touching them. In fact, trained by Adamenko, she discovered she could really move objects placed on transparent surfaces. Films of her demonstrations were shot in the early 1970s, and recently the previously mentioned *World of Discovery* documentary on Russian psychics had an interesting section devoted to her. Here she was presented as she is today, still demonstrating the same abilities for the camera. She took such objects as cigarettes, aluminum cigar tubes, and pens and put them on a Plexiglass plate suspended between two chairs; in such conditions she was able to make them rotate, roll, and move just by having her hand approach, but never touch, them. The demonstration was quite puzzling. It did appear very natural and repeatable and it seemed that the usual tricks (like secretly blowing on the surface to have the object move thanks to the air current thus created) were unlikely.

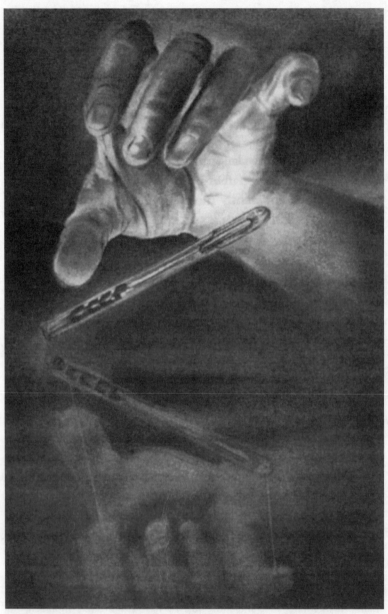

James Becker

Some time ago, I visited James Randi in Florida; he had recently returned from Russia, where he had gone for some filming to be included in *Nova*'s 1993 documentary about his work, "Secrets of the Psychics." Randi told me that, while he was there, the TV production staff approached Vinogradova and asked if she would agree to demonstrate her abilities on camera. She agreed; however, she put forth the condition that Randi had to be kept away from the room where filming was to take place. This was quite an inappropriate request, considering that the documentary was dedicated to Randi's investigations. Nonetheless, Randi accepted her veto: this way, she would present her demonstration as she always did, that is, not under controlled conditions. It was, in any event, an occasion to film her from different angles and to have better video material for study.

The segments filmed with Vinogradova were not included in the final documentary; however, Randi had copies of the original unedited footage that he was going to show me. Vinogradova was seen speaking, in Russian, with the operators, then walking back and forth on the thick carpet, combing her hair, and rubbing with a towel the surface of a Plexiglas plate placed on top of four glasses turned upside down on a table. Originally, she started to demonstrate her abilities with various objects: cigarettes, pens, plastic rings, a small wooden doll from a set of nesting dolls, a small hairspray bottle, and a glass. All objects moved quite freely, as seen in the other films; only the spray bottle and the glass, being the heaviest objects, moved little or only wobbled back and forth as she passed her hand over them. Suddenly, while moving the nesting doll, a white thread that was on the table, under the Plexiglas, was seen to be moving too, following the doll. I pointed this out to Randi and he told me that the cameraman, after shooting the film, told him that he had seen the moving thread but didn't realize that he had actually zoomed in on it and caught it on film. Randi himself hadn't yet had a chance to examine the film so he was quite interested too. "That thread," he told me, "was from the torn end of a cloth-based duct tape used to hold tiny microphones to the edge of the Plexiglas. The microphones were there to detect if she was doing any blowing to move the objects. The thread was not placed there purposely. It was just a loose thread. But, of course, it proved to be the indicator needed."

A Neglected Explanation?

Randi and I discussed the possibility of static electricity being solely responsible for the phenomena. In the *World of Discovery* documentary, this possibility was mentioned as an explanation proposed by skeptics, but it was immediately discarded since Vinogradova said she could move objects weighing up to two hundred grams. She claimed that it was impossible to do this using only static electricity. We thought we should try to repeat her performance with a Plexiglas plate, but, owing to other things we were involved with at the time, we didn't have a chance to get around to it before my departure.

Once back in Italy, I discussed the subject with my colleagues Luigi Garlaschelli and Franco Ramaccini of CICAP (the Italian Committee for the

Contributors

Paul Barber is a research associate with the Fowler Museum of Cultural History, University of California, Los Angeles 90024-1549, and author of *Vampires, Burial, and Death: Folklore and Reality*.

Barry Beyerstein is a faculty member and member of the Brain Behavior Laboratory in the Department of Psychology at Simon Fraser University, Burnaby, B.C. V5A 1S6, Canada.

Susan Blackmore is in the Department of Psychology, University of West of England, Bristol BS1 2JP, U.K.

Jan Harold Brunvand is professor of English at the University of Utah, Salt Lake City, UT 84112, and the author of many books on urban legends.

David Daegling is associate professor of anthropology at Yale University.

Hayden Ebbern is an undergraduate in the Department of Psychology at Simon Fraser University, Burnaby, B.C. V5A 1S6, Canada.

Thomas Gilovich is professor of psychology at Cornell University and the author of *How We Know What Isn't So: The Fallibility of Human Reason in Everyday Life*.

Justin Kruger is a doctoral student in social psychology at Cornell University.

James D. Livingston now teaches in the Department of Materials Science and Engineering at the Massachusetts Institute of Technology, and was for more than thirty years a physicist at General Electric's Corporate Research and Development Center. He is the author of *Driving Force: The Natural Magic of Magnets* (Harvard, 1996), a popular-science book on the history, legends, science, and technology of magnets.

Lynn McCutcheon taught psychology full-time for 23 years and currently teaches as an adjunct at Florida Southern College.

David Morrison is the Director of Space at NASA Ames Research Center, where he manages basic and applied research programs in the space, life, and Earth sciences, with emphasis on astrobiology—the study of the living universe.

Sean Mulligan is a graduate student in the Department of Biological Sciences at Simon Fraser University, Burnaby, B.C. V5A 1S6, Canada.

Joe Nickell is CSICOP's Senior Research Fellow and author of numerous books on the paranormal.

Massimo Polidoro is head of research at CICAP (the Italian Committee for the Investigations of Claims of the Paranormal), editor of its journal *Scienza and Paranormale*, author of various books dealing with paranormal claims, and a graduate student in psychology at Padua University.

Benjamin Radford is Managing Editor of the *Skeptical Inquirer*. After receiving a B.A. in psychology from the University of New Mexico in 1993, he traveled extensively pursuing his interest in urban legends.

Kenneth Savitsky is assistant professor of psychology at Williams College.

Daniel Schmitt is assistant professor in the Department of Biological Anthropology and Anatomy and heads the Vertebrate Movement Laboratory at Duke University Medical Center.

Trey Stokes has worked as a creature effects artist for such films as *Species, The Abyss, Batman Returns, RoboCop II*, and *The Blob*.

Irwin Tessman is a professor of biology. Address: Department of Biological Sciences, Purdue University, West Lafayette, IN 47907.

Jack Tessman is a professor of physics emeritus. Address: Department of Physics, Tufts University, Medford, MA 02155.

David E. Thomas works as a physicist in Albuquerque, New Mexico. He is a graduate of New Mexico Institute of Mining and Technology and is currently vice president of the New Mexicans for Science and Reason. He is also a *Skeptical Inquirer* consulting editor.